BRITISH MEN OF SCIENCE

General Editor
Sir Gavin de Beer F.R.S., F.S.A.
membre correspondant de l'Institut de France

Charles Scott Sherrington

Charles Scott
SHERRINGTON

An Appraisal

Ragnar Granit FOR. MEM. R.S.

*Professor of Neurophysiology, the Royal Caroline Institute,
and Director of the Nobel Institute for Neurophysiology, Stockholm*

Doubleday & Company, Inc.
Garden City, New York
1967

Printed in Great Britain

Contents

List of Plates

List of Figures

vii

Preface

This book has been written in response to a request from Sir Gavin de Beer. Even though the initiative was not my own, writing it has given me great pleasure, both because of its subject and because it has provided me with an opportunity of paying something of my life-long debt to British physiology. The Editor of the series wanted an appraisal, not a biography, and this agreed well with my own preferences. The main difficulty has been the need to define my reader. I have tried to solve this problem to the best of my ability but it remains to be seen whether my particular variety of humanity corresponds to anything found in real life. The learned may find the book too unsophisticated for their taste, the laymen, too learned. Biologists should be able to read it with little effort.

My plan is simple: firstly 'Personality and Background' followed by a sketch of the kind of physiology of the nervous system that Sherrington encountered in his youth. Then follow some chapters on his achievements and some on what is left over of his fundamental concepts in the present-day physiology of the nervous system. This is enough to make some of the chapters an easy introduction to much of what is relevant today in this complex field, in spite of the limitations imposed by this type of study. If those who are going to read the book as an introduction to modern neurophysiology find themselves compelled to make Sherrington's acquaintance at the same time, this should serve to enrich their experience of a great man and his nature. In his old age, Sherrington wrote a well-known book, *Man on his Nature*. My final chapter deals with this, his poems, and some other literary contributions.

There is a concise and excellent biography of Sherrington by his former pupil and successor in the chair at Oxford, Professor E. G. T. Liddell, in the *Obituary Notices of Fellows of the Royal Society*. Liddell has also written a *Discovery of Reflexes*. From both these sources I have borrowed a great deal for Chapters 1 and 2, and in addition their Author has been kind enough to serve as my chief consultant, an act of friendship deeply appreciated.

Mrs Lucia Fulton and the late John Fulton's former co-worker, Miss Madeline Stanton of the Yale Historical Library, have kindly given me access to the diaries and notes of Fulton. By courtesy of Professor Cameron, Master of Gonville and Caius College, Cambridge, I had a chance, in 1947, of seeing some material in the possession of Sherrington's old college, which I have used in the text. Sir Lindor Brown (Oxford) long ago sent me the records from a meeting of the Physiological Society at which Sir Charles Sherrington and Sir Henry Dale talked about old times in the Society, and Professor R. A. Gregory of Liverpool has provided me with some records from Sherrington's time at his University, including the type-script of a lecture by Professor K. J. Franklin overlapping with the theme of my book. I have used all this material, supplemented by some 'Boswelling' of my own—occasionally without specific quotations of source—in the first chapter. I wish here to put on record my gratitude for all these favours received.

This, however, does not complete my tally-sheet. I want to mention benevolent criticism of several chapters by Sir John Eccles (Canberra) and Professor Göran Liljestrand (Stockholm), valuable photographs, letters, comments, etc., by Professors E. N. Da C. Andrade (London), Sir Gavin de Beer (London), Derek Denny-Brown (Harvard), the late Alexander Forbes (Harvard), Sir Bryan Matthews (Cambridge), R. A. Morton (Liverpool), and Wilder Penfield (Montreal), friendly help by the Librarian of The Royal Society, Mr I. Kaye, and the Librarian of the Royal Society of Medicine, Mr P. Wade, B.A. I thank all of them for kind help willingly given.

I am greatly indebted to the following for permission to publish the Figures: Australian Journal of Science; Journal of Comparative Neurology; Journal of Neurophysiology; Journal of Physiology; Proceedings of the Royal Society; Quarterly Journal of Experimental Physiology; Johns Hopkins Press; University of Pennsylvania Press; and Yale University Press.

Finally I wish to thank my secretary, Miss Gunvor Larsson, for having typed the manuscript, and Mrs Evi Reigo and Mrs Anne-Marie Chöler for help with the Figures.

Stockholm, October 1963   RAGNAR GRANIT

For as long as our present Western culture can keep above water we shall be inwardly enriched by absorbing the colours and figures of the past and treating the intellectual conditions and transformations of earlier epochs as a great furtherance of our own intellectual consciousness.

—Jacob Burckhardt, *Judgements on history and historians.*
Allen & Unwin, Ltd., London, 1959
(Translations of *Historische Fragmente*, based on Burckhardt's lecture notes, Basel 1865–85.)

Chapter 1

Personality and Background

If it is true that most scientists have an optimum age at which they display their full powers, then what should be the criterion? Surely it must be maturity with creative faculties preserved. In Sherrington's case the curve of his scientific life slowly rose to a maximum during the twenty years after 1925. In 1927 he was seventy. In the first half of those twenty years he was surrounded at Oxford by a group of devoted pupils—himself old enough to sustain their admiration gracefully—and the work from his period of youthful inspiration rose to a second climax. The young, under his guidance, and profiting from technical advance, added precision and clarity to a conceptual world that he, with simpler tools, had created in the two decades on either side of the turn of the century. His laboratory radiated quiet enthusiasm, he must have felt like a master-builder watching his creation approach a final form upon his well-laid groundwork. Sherrington was still an active experimenter, even though his afternoons were often spent on committee work in London.

That period was harvest time in many other respects. Towards its close Sherrington gathered years of reading and study into two scholarly works, his Gifford Lectures, *Man on his Nature* in 1940, and *The Endeavour of Jean Fernel* in 1946, the latter in the eighty-ninth year of his life. In 1925 he had published *The Assaying of Brabantius*, a small collection of poems, humbly submitted to the world by C. S. Sherrington; few realized that the new poet was a celebrated man in his sixty-eighth year and, indeed, at the time President of the Royal Society.

Those who were his pupils and lived through that sparkling

sunset marvelled at the rich display of light and colour. One could but conclude that he had possessed spiritual resources strong enough to succeed in integrating into his life all his thinking, reading, and experimentation, in this way establishing the values that were worth living for to the end. His frail body, crippled by rheumatic disease, by deafness and an incipient glaucoma, was kept alive in that last decade by sheer spiritual strength. Yet he could still tell a good anecdote, laugh and listen when old friends or former pupils visited him in the nursing home at Eastbourne. When he died in 1952 at the age of ninety-four, the obituaries published in *Nature* all struck the same note. Lord Adrian underlined his wisdom and charity and said: 'he has set us all an example of how to accept our life, and we have lost one who was admired for himself as well as for his science.' I myself cannot improve upon what I said at the time: we shall 'always remember him as a man in whom the spirit, intellectually as well as emotionally, had explored all its boundaries and returned with unexpected resources of light and strength. Nothing human was alien to him'.

In the course of his life Sherrington acquired a rare virtue, one that scarcely enjoys respect in the modern world or at least is very seldom mentioned: he had piety or something akin to it. Certain past experiences to which he alluded in poetry ('for thee the gods had willed the steep descent and flowerless pit') may never be disclosed. More important is his own passionate reply as given in the same poem:

> Nay, heart be brave; console thee and be wise,
> wouldst let love's sacrifice go vain!
> Wait thou thine urn, with still averted eyes;
> thy tryst shall come; till then be this thy gain,
> that life's task dwarfs life's pain.
>
> *The Assaying of Brabantius*

In *Man on his Nature* he achieved the final synthesis. In personal intercourse his victory over himself emerged in his gentle smile and friendly manners, his generosity. With all this he did not belong to the meek and over-pliable. He had strong likes and dislikes and on the rare occasions when he criticized people, this served to expose their lack of sincerity or consideration.

The truth is, of course, that there can be no piety without passion ultimately conquered. Sherrington's capacity for emotional engagement in his old age was so much taken up by these intellectual pursuits which tend to stay with the truly intellectual to the very end, that one was apt to see in him merely the great sage commanding respect and veneration. He had, after all, lived through most of the major developments of modern science. There was in his bearing something of the absent-minded savant living in his own world of thought. Yet in conversation with those with whom he felt a bond of mutual interest or understanding he became the lovable companion of whom friends and pupils have written so affectionately. But one catches a glimpse of another Sherrington in his poetry, in early polemics with Horsley and Tait written at a time when he still had to rise in defence of his work. One meets this other man from a different angle in some remarks by a youthful contemporary and fellow-collegian (later, Sir) Squire Sprigge, who had been induced by Sir William B. Hardy to write down, late in life, what he remembered of the boy who in 1880 entered Cambridge University:

'Though Sherrington on all ordinary occasions was singularly gentle and courteous, he suddenly became a "devil incarnate" when the ball began to move at rugger. When the game was over he relapsed at once into his normal gentle, courteous self.'[1] At that time Caius was a great college for games and Sherrington a valuable member of its fifteen. He also rowed for his college. The 'fierce little forward' had joined Cambridge University as a non-collegiate student, 'very polite, shy and quiet'. He had become a member of Caius in his second year and almost immediately Science Scholar of his college. The following summer (1880) he obtained a First in Part I of the Natural Science Tripos. In due course (1883) he was similarly placed in Part II. 'The more men he knew the more friends he made, but it remained a small circle, and I doubt whether any of us except perhaps Threlfall ever realized what a great man was growing up among us.'

[1] It is interesting to note what Sherrington said about Sprigge: 'Something of a Beau Brummel—but on the field or court a hard-bitten player. He was a general favourite with us all, witty and companionable, one who never seemed to have any particular work to do.' (Sir Squire Sprigge's life-work came to be the editing of *The Lancet*.)

It may have contributed to his shyness that he did not come from one of the well-known public schools and directly to a college. Yet he did come from a first-rate and extremely ancient Foundation, Ipswich School, where the headmaster (1858–1883) of his time was Dr H. A. Holden, editor of *Aristophanes* and one of the greatest Greek scholars in England. Cardinal Wolsey, himself assumed to have been an old boy, had endowed the school richly, but little was left after the Cardinal's fall. Henry VIII maintained the old grammar school and Queen Elizabeth gave it a Charter in 1565. It gradually developed into a local institution for Suffolk and the town, espoused by the local people, merchants and scholars, who provided it with benefactions to enable Suffolk boys to complete their education at Cambridge. It was a school 'for the building of character rather than imparting of mere learning', but endowments from the local supporters also kept its equipment and teaching abreast of the times. The Governors were in the habit of leaving the Headmaster in full authority, free to develop the school as he thought best. It is questionable whether any of the public schools, as they were at the time, could have done better for a young mind, eager to learn and imaginative. Sherrington entered Ipswich School in 1871.

A good classical education such as Holden's school provided was then and still is an excellent antidote for the tendency of science to make its adepts too enthusiastic over disconnected facts or purely technological or practical goals. The classics tend to foster the attitude of the scholar with its emphasis on values, judgement and character. The view, prevailing today, may well have come down from Bacon who held the purpose of science to be 'none other than this, that human life be endowed with new inventions and powers'. This is precisely what is being overdone in the present age when specialization begins at school before body and mind are ripe. Wilder Penfield, one of Sherrington's best known pupils, goes as far as to state that 'Sherrington's career is a strong argument for the belief that a broad schooling in the humanities is the best preliminary training for medical men or for medical scientists'.

One of Sherrington's major assets in the study of the central nervous system was a synthetic attitude bent on emphasizing principles rather than *disjecta membra* of observation. The belief that for this he owed a debt of gratitude to his old school and the type of education it gave him may be difficult to prove, but many facts support it. How easily Sherrington fell into the rôle of a humanist and historian is shown by all his publications from the latter part of his creative life. None but a man well grounded in the classics could have written *Jean Fernel* and *Man on his Nature*. E. G. T. Liddell, in his masterly obituary, states that 'at Ipswich school, Thomas Ashe [the poet, who was one of his teachers] was a great inspiration to Sherrington and gave him a love of the classics and the urge to travel'. The former interest lasted throughout his life. When Lord Adrian and Alexander Forbes called on Sherrington at Ipswich, whither in 1938 he had retired, they found him engrossed in the study of Aristotle in preparation for his Gifford Lectures (Plate 2). Close ties with his old school were forged again: this time he served on its Board of Governors.

Sherrington's father, James Norton Sherrington of Great Yarmouth, died when his children were small, and so it befell that his stepfather was a great influence in his life. Dr Caleb Rose of Ipswich was said to have been a good classical scholar as well as an archaeologist. 'The home at Edgehill House was a rendezvous for artists, the rooms being crammed with the works of David Cox, Cotman and others of the Norwich school.' The influence of his stepfather can be traced in Sherrington's decision to take up medicine. It is known that Caleb Rose gave a copy of the English edition of Johannes Müller's *Elements of Physiology* to his stepson in 1879, one year before he matriculated at Cambridge.

Many elements in Sherrington's upbringing and inclinations might seem to have predestined him toward the humanities. He had the excellent memory requisite for the historian; he was a good draughtsman and acquired foreign languages easily. He was sensitive beyond the ordinary to aesthetic values. The young man's urge to do creative work should have been obvious within the family circle. His two brothers took up law. Dr Rose must have been a good judge of talent to divine the nucleus of a biologist within this richly faceted young mind, or perhaps his mother, whom he dearly loved, had powers of divination. Whatever the answer, there is one gift Sherrington must have possessed in an obvious manner from the very beginning, a talent that great biologists **can** hardly do without: an exceptionally observant mind. No one who has had the privilege of seeing Sherrington in the laboratory could fail to be impressed by the amount of detail he noticed in the movement of an animal, in some piece of tissue under the microscope, or in the general run of an experiment. What Darwin said about himself in his autobiography applies equally well to Sherrington: 'On the favourable side of the balance, I think that I am superior to the common run of men in noticing things which easily escape attention, and in observing them carefully.'

I recall one day in the early thirties in the Parks at Oxford. There had been some rain in the morning but when in the company of (now, Sir John) Eccles I walked home for lunch the lawns were steaming in the sunshine of spring. Suddenly there was Sherrington carrying an attache case, approaching us, a slightly built man with a preoccupied expression, gazing up at the sky. We had been striding along at a good pace, deeply immersed in talk, and taking very little note of what went on around us, nor did we imagine that our professor had done just that. He stopped, eyed us with an amused and friendly smile and unexpectedly said: 'Have you noticed that all the earthworms this morning are crawling in the same direction? Phototropism or what?'

This little incident also adumbrates Sherrington's capacity for translating observation into problem, a capacity that he retained to the end of his life as an experimenter. It is better called by its right name, a sense of wonder, a precious gift that distinguishes the truly creative from the merely talented. Wonder is the mind's finely sharpened point of contact with things unknown, but with advancing age the point tends to go blunt. Sherrington has written well on this theme: 'We dismiss wonder commonly with childhood. Much later, when life's pace has slackened, wonder may return. The mind then may find so much inviting wonder the whole world becomes wonderful. . . . But, greatest wonder our wonder soon lapses. A rainbow every morning who would pause to look at? The wonderful which comes often or is plentifully about us is soon taken for granted. That is practical enough. It allows us to get on with life. But it may stultify if it cannot on occasion be thrown off. To recapture now and then childhood's wonder, is to secure a driving force for occasional grown-up thoughts.' These thoughts were not too 'occasional' with Sherrington; 'habitual' would be a better word, and his sense of wonder lasted all his life. It was also no doubt the 'driving force' that maintained his state of latent intellectual curiosity, aroused into activity by provocations as slight as the passage of earthworms across his path.

Cambridge in the early eighties offered Sherrington instruction, inspiration and friendship. He became a member of a circle gathered around Sir Michael Foster (1836–1907), Praelector in Physiology. Sherrington once described this group, in conversation, as 'a nest of friends, I would like to say, real comrades' and Foster himself, in an obituary, as a 'personality that fascinated by a native dignity utterly free from any tinge of affectation or ostentation. His nature was brimful of kindliness . . . and charity towards people of every description'. The Praelector had been appointed in 1870 by Trinity College on a recommendation sought from T. H. Huxley. The post allows Trinity to call in a man for a specific task without requesting him to do anything for the College.

With Foster, who was the favourite pupil of William Sharpey, father of British physiology and Professor of General Anatomy and Physiology at University College, London, the Cambridge school inherited a sound tradition of experimentation. Foster had been persuaded by Sharpey in 1868 to become Professor of Practical Physiology in London, and so it cannot have been an easy decision for him to leave this appointment for a new enterprise and an apparently humbler position. The eminent mathematician, the Rev. Coutts-Trotter, who at the time was Vice-Master of Trinity and a 'man of unrivalled judgement', is said to have played a decisive rôle in inducing Foster to take a step that was something of a sacrifice. Its implications are briefly summarized in one short sentence by Sir Edward Sharpey-Shäfer of Edinburgh in his obituary of Foster (1907): 'English Physiology can never forget what it owes to Michael Foster.' The late professor of Edinburgh counted himself among the many people whose interest in physiology came from the personality and teaching of Foster. At University College, London, Foster was succeeded by Burdon Sanderson.

The Praelector was supposed to conduct classes in physiology, elementary biology and embryology. A small room, lent by the University, had been equipped for this purpose by the College. Through this initiative the College was in part responsible for many lines of inspired physiological research in Cambridge as well as elsewhere. Trinity has to the present day played a leading rôle in this field.

'Foster was not a great original discoverer of facts, though he was one of men' (Franklin). But he was a good teacher in possession of a fund of knowledge that, to judge by his famous *Textbook*, was both modern and well organized. His personal loyalty and genial ways pervaded his class and held the group together : 'when he was going to say something humorous, as he often did, he would pick up one corner of his beard and it was very entertaining, and then the joke would appear.' He became Professor of Physiology at Cambridge in 1883 and later M.P. for London University. Foster was 'a great organizer' and, at the time when Sherrington came up, 'busy with many things' and so could not himself devote much time to laboratory work.[1] Actually Sherrington 'never saw him do any demonstration'. Foster's *Textbook* of physiology first appeared in 1879 and in its seventh edition (1897) Sherrington was assistant author.

One of Foster's early discoveries at Trinity was W. H. Gaskell (1847–1914), B.A. in 1869 and 26th Wrangler in the Mathematical Tripos, whom he induced to take up physiology and later (1874) sent to Carl Ludwig's (1816–1895) famous laboratory in Leipzig for a year of training. Sherrington was greatly influenced by Gaskell, and since one of his best friends, C. S. Roy, the future Professor of Pathology at Cambridge, as well as his teacher in Strasbourg, F. L. Goltz, had also studied in Ludwig's laboratory it is worth rescuing from oblivion an anecdote that Sherrington credited to Roy (an eye-witness) and retold in his characteristic way, with the amused chuckle and the quick upward jerk of the head that preceded the climax.

One of the young men in Ludwig's laboratory was the Russian physiologist v. Cyon who once had a row with a big Austrian whose name Sherrington had forgotten. The disagreement became violent enough to lead to a duel. The small and lithe

---

[1] Foster was equally well known as a horticulturist, as I came to realize when trying to find out who the Foster was after whom a favourite in my garden (*Tulipa Fosteriana*) was named.

Cyon was an excellent swordsman and, while all the young men stood round and watched the fight, he hit his stout antagonist time and again with the foil, taking care not to hurt him. Disturbed by the shouts and laughter, Geheimrat Ludwig suddenly appeared on the scene and silence reigned. Ludwig somehow came to the conclusion that the real culprit was Cyon and gave him there and then a piece of his mind calling him a 'taugenichts' (good-for-nothing) and telling him to do a decent piece of work or else leave the laboratory. To this Cyon replied: 'Tomorrow, Herr Geheimrat, I shall make a discovery.' And, in point of fact, with his brother, he did discover that the effect of the accelerans nerve is abrogated by excision of the stellate ganglion, and, in conjunction with Ludwig, he discovered the depressor nerve in rabbits (Carl Wiggers).

This incident might leave Ludwig in a wrong light unless it be added that he was a most generous man who worked with his pupils and occasionally put his name on the paper but more usually let the pupil publish the paper alone and even went as far as to write it for him. This is as stated by Sir T. Lauder Brunton, who was in Leipzig 1869–70, and confirmed by Gaskell. The great German teacher was important enough to influence the whole of physiology of his period, directly or, as in the case of Sherrington, indirectly.

Foster also discovered J. N. Langley (1852–1925), at the time a young man of St John's College who had recently turned from the study of mathematics and history to natural science. He began attending Foster's classes in May 1873 and from then on was spellbound by physiology. Langley became a Fellow of Trinity in 1877 and gave the advanced lectures in physiology and histology for Foster. He became deputy to Foster in 1900 and in 1903 succeeded him as Professor. There was much general activity in this field at the time. The Physiological Society was founded in 1876 with Gerald F. Yeo, Professor of King's College, London, as its first Secretary. (Sherrington was to succeed him in 1889.) Physiology was therefore well under way at Cambridge when Sherrington turned up in 1880 to become Foster's third great discovery. On Langley fell most of the task of instructing the youngest devotee in the laboratory. The teacher was exacting, critical and not over-accessible, 'alert to people but I liked to be prepared,' said Sherrington, to whom

he was 'very kind and like an elder brother' (their age difference was five years), besides being a 'thoroughgoing instinctive
biologist'. At that time Langley was studying the secretory
activity of glands using the microscope as one of his major tools,
his first scientific interest and one that occupied him for some
fifteen years. Under his guidance Sherrington became a master
of histological technique and acquired a taste for histological
work that lasted all his life. As late as in 1940, after sixty years,
he published a paper with Sybil Cooper in which they described
the 'border cells' of the spinal cord. Langley's own major contribution which was on the autonomic nervous system came when
Sherrington had already embarked upon his own line of research.
Langley's experiments were carried out in part with (later, Sir)
Hugh Kenneth Anderson, who became Master of Gonville and
Caius College. Sherrington used to speak of him with considerable admiration.

The young men worked in small and uncomfortable rooms
and physiology as a science was not much in the limelight in
English medicine of the eighties. The great theoretical subjects
were bacteriology and pathology; the great international names
were Pasteur, Koch, Behring, Virchow.

One day a well-known physician from Glasgow, Professor
Gairdner, a man in his sixties, came down for a visit in the long
vacation and found all the young colleagues in the laboratories
engaged in active research. Sherrington as the youngest was
sent to show him round the place. Langley was engaged in a
very interesting experiment, recording saliva quantitatively
while stimulating the chorda tympani, and pieces of glands were
preserved for histological examination. Gaskell demonstrated
heart-block with the heart of a toad. Sherrington finally took the
visitor over to Anatomy and Pathology. On departing, Gairdner
asked Sherrington to explain to him what this queer business of
physiology was good for, as it seemed so far away from medicine.
In recalling that incident Sherrington laughed heartily and said:
'To think of it. I gather that heart-block nowadays is quite a
common disease and often curable. And there he saw those
experiments of Gaskell's.' Sherrington himself has retold this
with more detail in *Marginalia*.

At a meeting of the Physiological Society some sixty years
later Sherrington was induced to record his impressions of the

Society in the early eighties. Here are his words as taken down at the time:

> Looking back at these days, I mention three general impressions I had from them. One is and will always remain while I have a memory, the intimate, informal association of physiologists. Of course that could only have come from the older people and must have been their understanding and nature to make the younger feel at ease. . . . Well then, another impression that I have and I have it very strongly with those people . . . the people who had started it (the Society) and they were the older people, very much in earnest about it, . . . that I don't think they realised the magnitude—I think they were too modest to realise the magnitude—as it has proved, of what they were really cultivating. I think they did it just because they felt—and I am sure it was a general feeling of the time—that in our country physiology had been allowed to lapse . . . and they were really out to see what they could do in a quiet way . . . to get on with it. . . .And that brings me to the third point, that is very marked indeed: occasionally, not very often, there came some people from abroad,—and the welcome they got! Everybody was so delighted, so excited with the demonstration of the hospitality offered him. . . .

As an instance Sherrington mentioned a visit by Willy Kühne (1837–1900) of Heidelberg: 'a great linguist; he had translated Foster's book, and Langley and Lea had both worked with him.' This was the man whose excellent work on the retinal action potential, on visual purple and on the muscle's motor end-plates and sensory end-organs (the spindles) has had such a renaissance in our time. He was jovial and very fat, in fact— if the report is correct—they cut out a semicircle in his dining table to accommodate the expanded front (he was said to have such a dining table at home).

The impression one obtained from Sherrington when in private conversation he could be induced to speak about that period was that Gaskell, ten years his senior, was the man to whom everybody went for friendly advice, encouragement, and discussion of findings. 'Those who came under his influence can never forget his transcendent sincerity, his gift of sympathetic attention, and the unfailing wisdom of his advice.' These words, written by Sherrington's eminent contemporary and friend, the neurologist Sir Henry Head (1860–1940), recreate the warmth of feeling voiced also by Sherrington in speaking of Gaskell.

A living witness is Sir Henry Dale who, reminiscing in the company of Sherrington, among others, on October 1, 1941, at a meeting of the Physiological Society, called Gaskell 'the most stimulating advanced lecturer of physiology that you [Sherrington] or I ever have heard'.

It was not until the present day that Gaskell's greatest original discovery received full recognition. In studying the heart by stimulation of the vagus nerve, Gaskell (1887) found that a slow, positive change of potential could be led off from the sinus region of the heart when it underwent vagal inhibition. By the micro-electrode techniques of the present day this discovery has been fully confirmed (Katz, Hutter, and Trautwein) and further clarified, so that we now understand that Gaskell really was the first to demonstrate an active process of ionic exchange as the underlying mechanism for nervous inhibition.

In his obituary of Sherrington, Liddell quotes a letter from him to Sir Henry Head which seems to have been written at the time when the latter composed his appraisal of Gaskell. The letter begins:

Dear Head,
So busied have I been that I could not get to your note about Gaskell. He was *always* an inspiration to me and to any work I was able to try. Such inspiration is often subtle and part of its success springs, I imagine, from its subtlety. One does not like to be driven, but inspiration is *not* driving. My own work began by chance at the wrong end—the cortex-pyramidal degenerations, etc. It was certainly through Gaskell that I very soon felt that. One could not talk with him long without realizing that the cord offered a better point of attack physiologically. . . . [The letter ends] That gift of sympathetic attention, and unselfish switching off from his own problem to a pupil's, was characteristic of his nature. And his transcendent sincerity lent such force to his criticism or adhesion. He personified truth. In a hundred ways I owe him help and inspiration.

I wish that, when this war is over, some more adequate account of him and his influence may appear; no proper appreciation of him has been given yet.

Gaskell's work, after his period at Leipzig, on heart-block and on the myogenic origin of rhythms, as set up in different regions of the heart, has recently been given full acknowledgement by Carl Wiggers, an expert cardiologist, in his historical review of significant advances in heart physiology.

Gaskell next turned to the sympathetic nervous system and showed that it was of wholly spinal origin. But when W. Lee Dickinson and Langley discovered that nicotine selectively paralysed the nerve cells of the sympathetic ganglia, Langley was quick to see the analytical value of this finding, and with its aid soon demonstrated how the sympathetic system was designed, in particular that there was only one ganglion intercalated between the spinal cord and the peripheral goal. In fact, its functional anatomy that had been 'sheer confusion of obscurities and mistakes, he left perhaps the most clearly elucidated in the body' (Sherrington). Gaskell then turned to developmental morphology, but a book on *The Involuntary Nervous System*, drafted from his lectures, was published posthumously and still read in the twenties. (Looking up my own old copy I find it heavily underlined and annotated.) In this field Gaskell had a gifted pupil in (later, Sir) John Rose Bradford who studied the innervation of the blood-vessels of the lungs and the kidney, and who also soon found himself outpaced by Langley.

The rôle of any particular teacher as a source of inspiration is often better assessed in retrospect than at the time when young men are making their own careers. Sherrington's early publications and studies abroad suggest that he was slow in making up his mind as to whether he should turn to pathology and bacteriology or to the nervous system. Where the latter path would take him could hardly have been foreseen at the time, but later in life he clearly understood that Gaskell had given him good advice when he directed his interest to the spinal cord and discussed with him fundamental problems concerning inhibition. His early neurological work had by chance begun at the wrong end, he said, and the 'chance' was probably his association with Langley at a time when the latter had been given the task of examining the material obtained from a dog whose brain had been operated upon by Goltz of Strasbourg (to whom Sherrington also went for the winter 1884–1885). This examination, of course, led to a study of what he called 'cortex-pyramidal degenerations, etc.'.

Goltz's experiments on dogs, presented in London in 1881,

were designed to support the doctrine that there were no specific centres in the brain and that its whole mass was functionally equivalent. This view was strongly contested by (later, Sir) David Ferrier, who was able to fall back upon his own stimulation experiments which 'carried the day' and also the earlier experiments of Fritsch and Hitzig (1870), all of which had established functional localization of movement control, as it now seems, in no uncertain terms. There was also Hughlings Jackson's work on localized epilepsy (1869) which Ferrier knew well and referred to. So perhaps, after all, a learned historian and great histologist such as the late Stephen Polyak is right in speaking of the 'glaring inadequacies of Goltz's technique', adding viciously that 'even after Goltz had improved his technique, it would have been nothing short of a miracle, had his badly conceived and ineptly performed experiments resulted in anything but interference with the working of the entire brain'. Sherrington, however, spoke kindly of Goltz and visited him several times. Nevertheless, when much later he turned to brain research, it was the line of Fritsch and Ferrier that he was to follow. To Sherrington, David Ferrier was something of an idol. His experiments, carried out with Listerian precautions and on animals closer to the human type than the dog, played a great rôle in the development of brain surgery in England.

Sherrington had seen good experimentation done at home, in particular by C. S. Roy (1854–1897), of whom he said: 'As an operator in the laboratory he had no equal in this country,' and Roy, an admired friend, had been to Goltz's laboratory in 1879. This young man became the first Professor of Pathology in the University of Cambridge in 1884, at the age of thirty. He had also been the first recipient of the George Henry Lewes Studentship, founded by George Eliot for research in physiology, which Sherrington later held. With him and J. J. Graham Brown, an Edinburgh physician, Sherrington was to travel in Spain to investigate an outbreak of cholera in the summer of 1885. To judge by the obituary that Sherrington wrote about Roy, their friendship must have been intimate. There Roy emerges as a man of strong convictions, impetuous in acting upon them, and as an experimenter of exceptional ingenuity in devising apparatus and experiments, who was capable of making a name for himself in many fields in a short time: with J. J.

Graham Brown in studies on capillary blood pressure ('best data at the time'), in developing 'Roy's oncometer', known to all students of circulation, and in the discovery of an autochthonous rhythmic activity in the mammalian spleen. In 1890 Roy and Sherrington had published a paper together on the regulation of the blood supply to the brain. Roy had studied with Virchow and Du Bois-Reymond in Berlin, and with Julius Cohnheim in Leipzig he had carried out experiments praised by Kühne, Cohnheim, and Sherrington. Is it too much to assume that Roy who welcomed bacteriology but found it 'too tedious for his rapid and impulsive nature' should have tried to fire Sherrington's enthusiasm for it? Roy, himself a soul of fire, ex-surgeon in the Turkish army, a riding and sailing man, experimenting with everything from the design of flying machines to the hunting of the germ for cholera, must have been exciting company for Sherrington during the campaign in Spain. No doubt he became a friend whose influence counted. Nine years later Roy succumbed to a nervous breakdown from which he never recovered: he died after three years. Sherrington thought that Roy began to fail mentally in 1892. The picture of Roy and Sherrington (Plate 3) at the door of the Old Pathological Laboratory was taken in 1893.

During the Spanish expedition Sherrington is said to have met Ramón y Cajal, then at the very beginning of his career in neuroanatomy. In fact, in the year of their meeting, Cajal's autobiography mentions only two papers, both on cholera, and does not mention any meeting with Sherrington in Spain. The great work of the two men had not then risen above the horizon. Another outbreak of cholera took Sherrington to Venetia and Puglia and thence to visit Rudolph Virchow in Berlin, who sent him to Robert Koch for a six-week course in bacteriology. He stayed there a full year. In those days, at least in Koch's laboratory, bacteriological discoveries lay on the shelf, and once Sherrington actually took from the window-sill a piece of dust and cultivated a new species, apparently quite pleased with his finding. He showed it to Koch when the Professor went his daily round with his *Assistenten*, but had the bad luck to be accused by one of them of having stolen 'his bacteria'. Sherrington explained the situation and his account of what had happened was accepted by Koch, who in the end ruled that the other man should be allowed to continue with the work he had started on that same germ.

In his old age Sherrington praised Virchow for his courage in opposing Bismarck and thought it magnanimous of Virchow to suggest his going to work with Koch, especially as the two were on none too friendly terms with each other. This proposition suited Sherrington well as he was hoping to become attached to the Brown Institution of the University of London which had been founded in 1871 for research into diseases of animals useful to man (he became Superintendent in 1891). Koch asked him what he wanted to study and in the first instance he mentioned syphilis. Koch answered that this problem had been given to somebody else. Then he suggested glanders, but Koch thought it too contagious for a beginner. ('At the time I could hardly be called a beginner!') Finally he said he wanted to find out how bacteria passed through membranes, to which Koch said nothing. This advanced notion shows that Sherrington must have thought seriously of a future in bacteriology. Nor did German physiology at the Berlin institutions serve to entice him away from the sound grounding in that field under the guidance of Koch, though he went to Zuntz's classes in experimental physiology. Possibly, what he had in mind was a physiological approach to bacteriology, judging by his desire to study the passage of bacteria through membranes.

When back in England in 1887, the time had come for the final decision on how to make use of what he had studied and experienced. Sherrington had a flair for morphology and the microscope, but what he said about Roy need not be altered very much to suit himself. His was too active a nature to want to spend his life at the microscope. In retrospect we can clearly see that the two leading physiologists at Cambridge, Gaskell and Langley, also had in common a major interest in physiological function as reflected in anatomical organization. This is the typical problem of the biologically minded, how organization or form expresses itself in function. Under the influence of Gaskell, Sherrington chose to work on the spinal cord and set out on his scientific journey into the unknown, possibly not yet aware of how far Cajal had advanced on this route. The Spaniard's great moment came in 1889 when he collected all his 'scanty savings' in order to be able to go to Berlin and demonstrate his microscope slides to the leading histologists of the day: Weigert, Edinger, Held, Ehrlich, His, Schwalbe, Retzius, Waldeyer, and 'especially Kölliker', who became his scientific godfather. These names stand for most of the information that at the time was available to a young man keen on making some sense out of the intricate networks and cells in nervous centres. Cajal, the incomparable master of the silver stain, was later to provide Sherrington with the very precise pictures of organization of nerve terminals which were necessary for conceptual advance. Sherrington's early papers were still very much influenced by Gaskell's ideas and his studies of ganglion cells at the periphery of the antero-lateral column in the spinal cord of the alligator. This the younger man followed up in mammals. In his old age he returned to them once more.

In speaking of Gaskell, Sherrington emphasized his sincerity and so did Henry Head. This was something Sherrington greatly valued and it meant much to him both to do a piece of work well once it was undertaken, and to appreciate what other people did, felt, and stood for, as long as their attitudes had full resonance in their honesty. He was easily roused to admiration of everything genuine, but turned critical or silent whenever a false note of flippancy or glibness was struck, whatever the subject discussed. I can remember, for instance, hearing him criticizing on those grounds Lytton Strachey's portrait of General Gordon in *Eminent Victorians* and some of Bernard Shaw's writings. Sherrington's general attitude in such matters emerges from the description of an incident that befell him at an early period of his life when he had entered St Thomas's Hospital in London for the clinical part of his studies. This is related in his *Marginalia* (1953).

On his first night the bell rang and Sherrington went out, called to a childbirth, and found three families living in a roomy cellar lit by two naked gas flames. All went well and when he prepared to leave, just before daybreak, the young husband insisted on seeing him back to the hospital and carrying his bag. 'Back at the Hospital we parted with a handshake, and I could have cried "Concitoyen", I admired him so.' It was ten o'clock in the morning before he woke, the daily poker party of the young doctors was in full swing, the voices, the rattling of pence. 'The trivial vulgarity of the scene I woke to contrasted dreadfully with the dignity of poverty I had glimpsed hardly half a mile distant up the road.'

This is not the voice of a self-righteous man but that of a poet deeply aware of life's difficulties and sensitive to people, their needs, feelings and motives for action. His capacity for engagement on behalf of a cause that appealed to him in this manner could be illustrated by many other incidents from his life, well known to those around him and sometimes recounted in memoirs written at the time of his death. During the First World War, for instance, he went out for three months as a day-labourer to the Vickers-Maxim shell factory in Birmingham, did a 12-hour shift with the others and lived and worked with them. This was ostensibly in order to study industrial fatigue but a deeper motive surely was a desire to do something with his own hands to help the war effort at a time when young men sacrificed themselves in the trenches. The despair of relative inactivity cut deep into his whole being. I can still vividly remember the expression on his face, after the last war, when he looked up at me and said with an earnest voice, 'if you had lived your life in this country, you would realize that to us no sacrifice is too great when it comes to preservation of freedom'.

Personalities of striking intellectual power are rich or interesting in proportion to the number of conflicting forces or inner tensions they have mastered and moulded into a not too precarious state of balance, which is by no means the same as flattening out conflict by excessive devotion to scientific work. The wide emotional register of a Sherrington, a Ramón y Cajal, a Pascal is one of the traits most difficult to reconcile with what is known about their work as great experimenters or accurate thinkers in wholly unemotional terms. Yet these men did achieve strength and clarity in their particular fields, without compromise, and without shunning the issue by ending up in self-combustion or in the theatricals so characteristic of many *dei minores* on the scientific stage. If the synthesis such men achieve is rare, so also is the result, regarded as a work of creative imagination. 'What is good in people—and consequently in the world—is their insistence on creation, their belief in friendship and loyalty for their own sakes. . . .' These words by E. M. Forster are from an essay in which he expresses his belief in an aristocracy not 'of power' but 'of the sensitive, the considerate and the plucky' with 'power to endure'.

With these all too brief remarks I have tried to present something essential of Sherrington's personality, something that will serve well as an introduction to my presentation of him in the laboratory as I myself saw him at the end of the twenties.

Sherrington taught and worked in many places: as Lecturer in Systematic Physiology at St Thomas's Hospital and as Fellow of his old college in Cambridge from 1887; at the Brown Institution already mentioned; from 1895 as Holt Professor in Physiology at Liverpool, where much of his greatest work was done; and finally, from 1913, as Waynflete Professor of Physiology at Oxford, where he was a Fellow of Magdalen College.

He was never known as a good lecturer. His mind was too intricate and his imagination too powerful to keep in step with the spoken word bridled into the service of didactics. The subject was approached from many angles, and many reservations precluded pronouncement and simplification, since, after all, with Sherrington honesty could never be sacrificed in the interest of clarity. Honesty had to be satisfied. The course of the lecture was set out in advance on the blackboard, point by point; but as he went on, absent-mindedly, as if listening to some inner voice from a gnome whispering in his ear, he might at any time become fascinated by it rather than by his students, and begin delivering this inside display as a discourse meant for himself, and for those who were advanced enough to be able to play up to his game. To the well-prepared, familiar with his writings and thinking, this was pure delight and the most enjoyable part of his lecturing, but it was beyond the level of the undergraduates. His little gnome was in the habit of jumping intermediate steps in a logical sequence, just as the trained mathematician does when he says that one formula obviously follows from another, while the beginner may have to work hard for some time with pencil and paper to deduce the same result.

Sherrington himself can hardly have been aware of his weaknesses as a lecturer because his conscience constantly urged him to do his best. This form of instruction simply did not suit his nature, but he gave full compensation when he taught in the classroom. I doubt whether the science of physiology has ever seen experimental classes as well run as were those of the Sherrington school at Oxford. From the Professor down to the 'lab boys', firmly ruled by his old Assistant Mr Cox, everybody contributed his full share of interest and instruction. At the head of it all was a man who had lived through a large part of the classical epoch of physiology, and so the experiments designed for repetition belonged to him in a personal sense which later generations cannot experience. In the laboratory of this old man the world of physiology was as young as on the spring day of its creation. The book called *Mammalian Physiology* was published from Sherrington's practical instructions to his students and the illustrations of experiments were taken from work done in the classroom by them. Mr Cox, who oiled the wheels of the whole organization, had been with Sherrington from his early days at St Thomas's. It is said that the American neurosurgeon Harvey Cushing tried to offer Cox a better-paid post in his own service but was unsuccessful (reminding one of Lord Peter Wimsey's valet Bunter in a similar situation, 'I hope I know, Sir, when I am well situated').

Many of Sherrington's pupils have written in an inspired way about their master and I can only add one more of these personal testimonies to the rest. At the back of all these writings there is the impact of his personality, unassuming, generous, loyal to friends (among whom he counted pupils with serious interests in science), always willing to share with them his comprehensive knowledge that was supported by a phenomenal memory, Penfield said 'it excelled that of any man' he had known.

The head of a department responsible for the general direction of research within a group of young men can justly be praised if he succeeds in maintaining in his laboratory an atmosphere of sincere enthusiasm tempered by criticism and knowledge as Sherrington did. No ponderous manners for him. In every act he testified to the truth of Renan's words: 'I know that never has a truly great man himself believed that he is great and those who in their lifetime graze their reputation like green forage can be sure that it will not form ears to be harvested when they are dead.'

In his old age Sherrington once wrote to me: 'My observations and views can pass on a domestic standard but are not of any public value. They have served in their time to stimulate, and so far so good. But their simple technique is already out-of-date—vieux jeux.' There was real humility behind those words, though mingled with an old man's feeling of powerlessness accentuated by his realization of what was important and worth doing by the new methods which he lived long enough to see. These remarks he once supplemented in conversation by pointing out that what most struck him, as he grew old in his science, was that one saw so much that one thought should be done and also some possible new approaches to the old problems, but that one's training gradually became outdated by recent developments and so one became incapable of doing the really worthwhile things.

There may be a kind of negative feedback, mounting with age, in a man's scientific work. If so, it merely served to keep Sherrington for a long while on a stabilized level of excellence. In his seventies he would come into the laboratory and ask a young man 'what have you on' and, being told 'what was on', he pulled out a long lead-pencil from his pocket and began drawing on the nearest wall to illustrate his thoughts, getting excited himself as he threw out suggestions, giving vivid accounts of old experiments from the literature or of his own findings and punctuating his comments with an amused chuckle when he arrived at something that had caught his fancy. At this moment the listener was quite willing to laugh with Sherrington at whatever it was, because every incident was remembered with such remarkable visual detail and retold so vividly that he, too, had lived through every changing mood of Sherrington's mind. In this way the discussion would go on for a while, because the Professor also listened attentively to the younger man whom he excited and animated, until the moment came when he felt that something sensible had emerged out of it or he remembered something else he had to do. At that moment he suddenly turned round with an absent-minded unseeing glance and quickly disappeared. And the young man felt that scientific experimentation, after all, was a noble occupation. Why, if it meant so much to a man, so gifted and well-educated, and of the age and experience of his master, wouldn't it be good enough for himself!

What did Sherrington look like? There is a drawing of him

by R. G. Eves in *Selected Writings*, edited by Denny-Brown, which is an excellent likeness. The photograph in Liddell's obituary also seems very good to me, as does the one I have included in this appraisal of his work (Plate 1). The painting by Augustus John in the University Club of Liverpool is not the Sherrington his friends and pupils knew. Sherrington himself did not like it. The portrait at Burlington House by R. G. Eves shows him as more solemn than he used to be. Of portraits in words one of the best is by Denny-Brown in an obituary which is also comprehensive and rich in other ways, for all its brevity:

He was short in stature, about 5 feet 6 inches, very precise and neat in all his movements, and he tended to peer through rimless spectacles though not severely shortsighted. He had lively, humorous grey eyes and a light, easy, friendly manner. He was one of the mildest men I have ever known, rarely being vexed and at most saying, 'Dear me' or 'That is most annoying'.

To this characterization a few words by Liddell, who knew him so well, might be added:

Beneath that genial exterior there was, however, a well-balanced highly critical mind. There had to be. He was highly critical all his life of his own work, viewing it from every angle, and making it true and good; and he was just as critical of the work or thoughts of others, but in the wisdom of maturity he sealed his lips against criticism of those others. He could have broadcast many a pithy judgement, but he felt that to speak thus would have bruised and not cured. So with only a few was this special wisdom shared.

There are innumerable letters in existence from Sherrington to his friends and pupils, most of which are too intimate to be published at present, but the one chosen below as an example of his style of writing is of some general interest because it was written at the time when he had decided to retire from his chair at Oxford:

July 15, 1934

My dear Granit,

thank you much for your letter. It reaches me here [at Droitwich Spa] and it gives me real pleasure to receive it. I feel that I do not truly deserve such forgiveness for my long silence, on paper only for we have often talked of you in the Laboratory.

I am under treatment here—the saline baths are strong and do me good. I had a long illness this spring and last winter from rheumatism. When I got back to Oxford everyone was so kind and especially my colleagues in the laboratory and now comes your own charming and encouraging letter. When at last, I got back to the laboratory this summer I found everyone going on so well *without* me that the inference is clear. I am no longer of any *use* there and I should retire at once. But I have been persuaded, against my stricter judgement, to continue for another year! Forgive please so much about myself.

It makes me very glad that your evidence of inhibition [in the retina] becomes so strong. The nervous region in which you are examining it is in many ways especially suitable to determining the essential features of inhibition as presented by the nervous system; and so we are living, surely, in a memorable period just arrived for these studies, because it seems that the relative isolation from chemistry which such studies as yours (and Eccles' and Adrian's) stood in, may now be bridged by these recent results of Dale and his collaborators on 'excitation' and acetylcholine. The acetylcholine story suggests to the imagination that an 'esterase' may be the agent of mechanism of inhibition. The opposition of *electrical* sign for E and for I respectively which you find, if we can connect it with the chemical aspects in view of Dale's 'acetylchol.' excitation, may prove a key to the whole mechanism of both Exc. and Inh. It seems almost inevitable, does it not, that if the mechanism, chemical or physical, of either E or I is discovered, even merely in outline (but 'principiell') that discovery must almost contain (or involve) the finding out of the other, namely *I* or *E*?

Surely this spirited comment on essential problems of excitation and inhibition shows why he was persuaded against his 'stricter judgement' to give the laboratory one more year of his experience.

This brief presentation of his personality and background would be incomplete if the open house he and Lady Sherrington kept for friends, visitors and members of the laboratory was not mentioned. Sunday teas were gay occasions in their happy home, her liveliness and his geniality setting the tone of conversation. 'By many of those visitors Sherrington will be best remembered as brimming joyously with vivid memories of places and people and full of shrewd forgiving reflexions on the ways of mankind. By closer friends he will be remembered for an unsurpassing warmth of affection, a genial generosity of advice and time. He practised straightforward self-effacing friendship' (Liddell).

Chapter 2

The Scientific Background

In reviewing Cajal's autobiography (in 1937) Sherrington chose to quote a few sentences in which the old savant, not without an element of wistfulness, meditated on the fate of scientific work:

It is certain and even desirable that in the course of time my insignificant personality will be forgotten; with it will doubtless perish many of my ideas. In spite of all the blandishments of self-love, the facts associated at first with the name of a particular man end by being anonymous, lost for ever in the ocean of Universal Science. The monograph impregnated with individual human quality becomes incorporated, stripped of sentiments, in the abstract doctrine of the general treatise. To the hot sun of actuality will succeed the cold beams of the history of learning.

I was reminded of this quotation when a young colleague some time ago said to me: 'How good that you are going to write something about Sherrington. We [his generation] don't know anything about him.'

The only possible answer was to point out that a large number of the concepts this young man himself used in his thinking and experimentation had been created in Sherrington's mind; the rest of this book will be devoted mainly to an elaboration of this reply. Yet for my own purposes I turned his remark over in my mind and suddenly felt how difficult it is in science to re-create a state of ignorance once it has been honourably buried, especially so when, as in the case of Sherrington, there are no really dramatic experiments to fall back upon but rather a large number of analytical steps which in the end led him to a conceptual reorientation and to 'understanding', that final goal of our pursuits.

Even at the time when, at Liverpool, Sherrington did his most important work it cannot have been easy to see what he was trying to establish, since much of it merely looked like repetition of experiments which had already been performed by others. After a visit in 1901 an eye-witness as well prepared as Harvey Cushing wrote down: 'Sherrington is a great surprise. He is young, almost boyish if 36 (?) [actually 43], nearsighted, wearing, when he has not lost them, a pair of gold spectacles. He operates well for a "physiolog" but it seems to me much too much. I do not see how he can carry with any accuracy the great amount of experimental material he has under way. . . . As far as I can see, the reason why he is so much quoted is not that he has done especially big things, but that his predecessors have done them all so poorly before.' In the end Cushing, who stayed for a month and worked with Sherrington on chimpanzees, began to see what it was all about and wholly changed his opinion of him. They became very good friends and corresponded intermittently in affectionate terms.

What is so difficult to resuscitate in forgotten views and hypotheses is the particular state of intellectual tension in which those alive at the time experienced new facts and the pleasure of fitting them into their world of ideas and how they planned for new experiments calculated to render fresh advance possible. 'A thought,' says A. N. Whitehead with feeling, 'is a tremendous mode of excitement. Like a stone thrown into a pond it disturbs the whole surface of our being,' more so, one might add, in young workers than in those who have had this excitement several times over. There is also in the attitudes of young men preparing themselves for a life of scientific endeavour a revolutionary element of protest. They refuse to bow to the perspicacity of the parent generation and the probable reason for their recalcitrance is their awareness of possibilities which their predecessors have ignored or, for technical reasons, could not or would not investigate. This attitude leads to an emotional engagement of the whole personality and provides the inspiration which sustains the dull routine and hard labour involved in the experimentation needed to reach the discoveries looming on the horizon.

Sherrington was of the visionary type, more inspired by new ideas than by technical possibilities. He never took to the electro-physiological approach though always careful with the techniques he used, so we have to ask: what motivated him? What was the vision he tried to reach? In what sense was he unique among his contemporaries? To answer these questions one should describe in some detail the background of knowledge in his postgraduate days. The sketch that follows is brief and much imbued with the spirit of compromise.

There is a general problem involved in any situation where gifted young people reshape an established order; why did the previous generation fail to do it? Very often we find that the pioneers who laid the groundwork had so many pieces of the next puzzle at their disposal that it would seem to have been an easy matter to insert them and so advance the few steps needed to complete the next great generalization. Why this curious limitation to which even the greatest minds seem to be subjected? They stop suddenly and there is often no other obvious explanation than that fresh minds are required for the new effort; perhaps freshness as such is what is wanted.

This general situation recurs with the young Sherrington, though it is a little difficult to define against the complex background of neurophysiology in its formative years, unless more space be given to historical matters than is possible here. It is, in fact, the question Cushing was up against and first failed to understand. The general aspects of it are easier to grasp with the aid of an example from Sherrington's time but not from his own field. By taking a case that can be summarized in a few sentences, the analogous relation of Sherrington to his predecessors will in the end stand out the clearer.

Robert Koch as well as von Behring, inventor of the antitoxin for diphtheria, had both seen that animals which had been twice injected with immunizing sera often died after the second injection. Charles Richet's was the fresh mind which realized that the animal had not merely become enfeebled by the first dose but actually fell victim to a specific immunological reaction that he named 'anaphylaxie' and proved to be a real change in blood chemistry, caused by the initial injection. Richet's work was done with repeated injections of extracts of a sea anemone. Later on he had a suspicion that possibly the blood of one normal dog injected into another might prove poisonous, but he failed in the attempts to substantiate this hypothesis. Again a fresh mind was required, that of the Austrian Karl Landsteiner, to discover that in transfusion one man's blood actually is fatal for another's unless the two belong to the same blood group or either of them has 'neutral' blood. Thus Landsteiner, and not Richet, became the discoverer of the human blood groups. (Richet was a contemporary and friend of Sherrington, seven years his senior and often his host in Paris.)

The fresh mind of Sherrington would have found in textbooks by, for instance, Johannes Müller, Schiff, Vulpian, Claude Bernard, Foster, and others, many facts and ideas which could be called fundamental, important, interesting, or perhaps merely suggestive. Some of them will be mentioned in due course. Advance must have been slow because Foster's book in 1879 contains very little on the nervous system and the spinal cord that is not found in Schiff's *Lehrbuch* (1858–1859) and Vulpian's *Leçons* (1866). Sherrington had become personally acquainted with Moritz Schiff in Goltz's laboratory and described him to John Fulton as 'almost a dwarf, rather stout and possessed of penetrating black eyes which sparkled in a most extraordinary fashion'. According to Liddell Sherrington had read Vulpian's *Leçons sur la physiologie générale et comparée du système nerveux* (1866) as a young man and remembered it with pleasure all his life. No wonder, because the book is attractively written and proceeds from experiment to experiment, being the text to demonstrations which Vulpian gave when deputizing for Claude Bernard at the Sorbonne. Liddell reviews the book in considerable detail. It is nevertheless easier to form a precise opinion of the state of knowledge of muscle and nerve physiology from the first volume of Schiff's *Lehrbuch der Physiologie des Menschen* (1859), whose approach is modern in its insistence on evidence and in distinguishing between facts and hypotheses.

'The age in which Sherrington lived as a young man is remote indeed from the present, for in his early days there was no certainty that nerve fibres always belonged to nerve cells' (Liddell). Vulpian had hazy notions about the 'granular matter' of the spinal cord but the clear-headed Schiff, six years earlier, had written that the grey matter with its multipolar cells is the site of reflex activity but that this cannot as yet be regarded as rigorously proved. Vulpian failed to see the significance of one of the major discoveries of that age, Augustus Waller's demonstration in 1851 that cut nerves degenerated peripheral to the section and only in that portion. Schiff understood that this meant that the peripheral portion had been isolated from a trophic centre. Wallerian degeneration, as it came to be called, was launched a little too early; there was not yet enough of a spinal cord histology to make it useful. Marchi presented his universally applied method of studying nerve degenerations in 1886.

In the first edition of Foster's *Textbook* which Sherrington read at Cambridge the nervous system still appeared as a 'protoplasmic network' which 'so to speak, [is] mapped out into nervous mechanisms by the establishment of lines of greater or less resistance, so that the disturbances in it generated by certain afferent impulses are directed into certain efferent channels. But the arrangement of these mechanisms is not a fixed and rigid one.' Foster thus, for very good reasons, avoided speaking in precise terms. None were available.

Briefly, one might say that the reflexology Sherrington encountered in his early studies was an experimental science based on gross anatomy. Before him one generation of physiologists had already sectioned and stimulated the efferent and afferent roots of the spinal cord as well as various nerves. Schiff, for instance, knew the ataxia following acute (afferent) dorsal root section; for the violent priority fights in which he and Brown-Séquard were involved in matters concerning the effects of sections and semisections of spinal columns (see Liddell's monograph) this little book cannot find space. 'The rights and wrongs of these past quarrels [says Liddell] are difficult to assess now, especially in a quest which relies on partial spinal sections, but there is no doubt that Brown-Séquard was a pungently able advocate of his own achievements and won the permanent label of "Brown-Séquard syndrome" for the anteroposterior semisection of the cord: i.e. loss of sensation on the opposite side below the lesion, and retention and even increase in sensation on the same side, with motor paralysis on the side of the lesion.'

Luck in science has a tendency to favour the well-prepared mind; this was certainly true of Sherrington, the trained microscopist turned physiologist, who was ready at the starting-line when the great era of creative cellular histology began and problems concerning the structure of the central nervous system rose to actuality. Though he had given up pathology and bacteriology, they had at least made him look on cells as familiar objects. His work on 'cortex-pyramidal degenerations' in Goltz's laboratory and at Cambridge must have contributed to the same goal. And so, when on Gaskell's advice he decided to attack the physiology of the spinal cord, he brought to the subject fresh insight into the necessity of knowing its cellular organization before further advance could be made. From gross anatomy he turned to thinking in terms of histology.

The nerve cell with its interconnections became his analytical unit. This was Sherrington's first great notion, one of his main contributions to neurology.

The obvious parallel with developments in physics and chemistry towards unitary analysis need hardly be elaborated. Something of the delight he felt when the application of this incisive point of view ultimately became fruitful echoes in the opening sentence of his Silliman Lectures (1904) which later (1906) became the book *Integrative Action of the Nervous System*: 'Nowhere in physiology does the cell-theory reveal its presence more frequently in the very framework of the argument than at the present time in the study of nervous reaction.' If at the time this was a pertinent observation, his was the imaginative work which had made it so. Sherrington grew slowly into the full consequences of this approach to physiological problems. The basic experiments were carried out at the turn of the century, but the ones that really directed developments in the physiology of the central nervous system towards the analysis of unitary behaviour were performed in the twenties, at Oxford. The full significance of years of experimentation guided by sound intuition then became obvious to physiologists all over the world, and Lord Adrian's work at Cambridge supplemented that of the Oxford school.

When Sherrington started experimenting, the nerve-cell or neurone theory did not exist. But by the instinct (for want of a better word for a man's inaccessible mental activity) that guides the true scientist, Sherrington laid out his course from the very beginning in such a fashion that he was able to avail himself of every parallel advance in the histology of the spinal cord, being a good enough histologist to be able to sift the wheat from the chaff.

Thus it is in the history of histology that we have to look for the background of some of Sherrington's fundamental ideas and, having to start somewhere, there is no-one better than Johannes Müller (1801–1858) to deserve the honour of being singled out as a pioneer. How deeply Müller, who was professor at Bonn and ultimately in Berlin from 1832, influenced physiology and histology may be seen from the impressive list of some of his famous pupils: von Helmholtz, Brücke, Ludwig, Virchow, Schwann, Henle, Reichert, von Kölliker, Remak, Traube, Du Bois-Reymond, J. Meyer, Lieberkühn, Hannover, von Graefe and Max Schultze. 'When I look back,' said Hermann von Helmholtz, then at an age of seventy, 'upon my own under-graduate days and the impression a man like Joh. Müller, the physiologist, made upon us, I would especially like to emphasize one point. Whosoever at any time has come in touch with one or several men of the first rank, his spiritual standards ('geistiger Masstab') will be changed for the rest of his life; moreover, such contact is the most interesting experience life has to offer.' Another pupil, Du Bois-Reymond, discoverer of the nerve's action current, who succeeded his teacher in the chair of physiology in Berlin, in an eloquent speech compared Müller's intellectual conquests to the empire of Alexander, which after his death had to be divided among his generals as none of them was capable of ruling it alone. One might add that Alexander's generals are forgotten but many of Müller's pupils have a place for ever in the history of four sciences, physiology, anatomy, pathology, and physics.

Müller, father of German physiology, was primarily an anatomist and several of his pupils took up the study of histology. Purkinje, in 1837, had described the cerebellar cell that bears his name, but Müller's pupils followed close on his heels; Remak (1838), Schwann (1839) and Helmholtz (1842) investigated nerve cells using the new compound achromatic microscope which Purkinje, in a letter to his friend Anders Retzius in Stockholm, had described so enthusiastically. Adolph Hannover, a young Dane, had studied with Müller in Berlin and upon his return began staining nerve cells with chromic acid and got pictures in which the processes extended to greater length than anyone had seen before. von Kölliker (1817–1905) during a long life devoted to the study of cells became the foremost histologist of his time, and for decades his *Gewebelehre* was the leading textbook on the subject.

Liddell, in his monograph, emphasizes the contribution of Deiters, 'the forgotten histologist', as he calls him. This man, who died from typhus in 1863 at the age of twenty-nine, worked in the laboratory of Müller's former student, Max Schultze, whose fame today rests on his demonstration of different receptors in the eyes of nocturnal and diurnal animals, 'rods' dominating in the former, 'cones' in the latter. The retina has always been regarded as a difficult histological preparation and so it comes as no surprise that the histological technique was at an advanced stage in Schultze's laboratory. Deiters hardened his preparations in chromic acid, stained with carmine, and made serial sections and so was able to distinguish the nerve cell's 'cylindraxis prolongation' or axon from the 'protoplasmic prolongations' or dendrites. Deiters was emphatic that nerve-cell bodies give origin to nerve fibres; also the nerve fibre which leaves the spinal motor nerve cell passes on to take its place in the spinal nerve root, emerging from the ventral horn. 'Deiters paid much attention to the problem of anastomoses between ganglion cells in the central neuraxis, and said firmly that previous work which was claimed to support such an idea was founded on grave error', having in this criticism the full support of von Kölliker's authority.

Clearly it is impossible here to trace in detail the development of our knowledge about nerve cells and their interconnections, and unnecessary at that, since it has been done so well by Liddell in his monograph. The improvement in staining methods and embedding of the preparation gradually brought clarity, and when von Recklinghausen in 1860 introduced silver staining, the stage was set for the final act. Was the reflex that began with an afferent inflow through the dorsal roots really elaborated in a 'protoplasmic network', containing lines of 'greater or less resistance', before it emerged through the ventral spinal roots to activate its effector organ? Or were the nerve cells independent and merely provided with points of contact?

For Sherrington it was essential to know exactly how nerve

cells were interconnected. We, his successors, would like to think that the formidable task of making some sense out of an organ containing some ten thousand million nerve cells must have appeared to him, as it does to ourselves, nearly hopeless if these cells in addition were organized as a protoplasmic network, as they would be according to the so-called reticularist point of view.

Intuitively Sherrington headed straight for the contact or neurone theory, even before strict proofs were available. There was one very good argument in favour of this notion: Waller's fine discovery (Wallerian degeneration) which had shown that degenerations generally stopped short of the next neurone.

In 1875 the eminent Italian histologist Camillo Golgi (1843–1926) introduced his silver chromate stain, an elegant but capricious method, which has survived to this day in various modifications because, when successful, it stains the ramifications of the nerve cells. Golgi found the nervous structures to consist of cell body, axon and dendrites (Fig. 1) thus confirming the 'forgotten histologist'. Golgi saw two types of nerve cells. One type may for the present purpose be exemplified by the ventral horn cell or motor neurone possessing dendrites branching in the spinal cord and a long axon which (in this particular case) runs out in the periphery to form so-called motor endplates on muscle fibres. The other type of neurone has a dense network of short branches and also a brief axon. Many intercalary or interneurones belong to this type. However, in the end Golgi came out in favour of protoplasmic anastomoses within a neuropile or reticulum and became the leading reticularist of the day.

Opposition to the reticularist point of view soon began to gather force. In 1886 and 1887 Forel and His, both histologists of the first rank, concluded from their own material that the anastomoses between nerve cells did not exist. Consequently neurones must be linked by contact .This is the basic proposition of the neurone theory that Waldeyer later (1891) enunciated in a review of Cajal's work—officiously it seems, because Liddell's analysis of the literature, in agreement with Cajal, shows that Waldeyer himself did nothing but invent a name for the contact theory, which at the time had behind it the full strength of Cajal's work and argumentation.

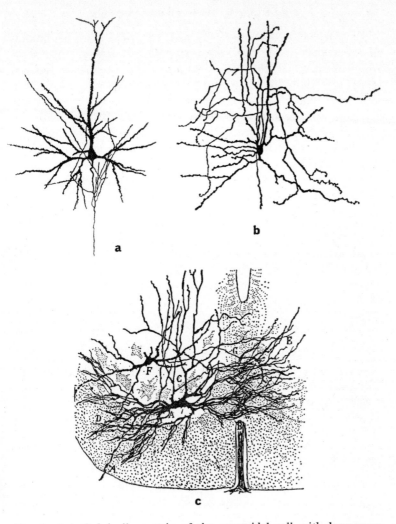

Fig. 1 (a) Golgi silver stain of the pyramidal cell with long axon (pointing downwards) from the visual cortex of the cat. The axon is provided with a branch returning towards the dendritic region of the cell. This is called a *recurrent collateral*. (By courtesy of the late D. A. Sholl, University College, London.) (b) Golgi stain. Cell from the cortex of the cerebrum. It belongs to Golgi's Type II and has a short axon, hardly distinguishable from dendrites. (c) Golgi stain. Cross-section through the ventral portion of the spinal cord of newly born dog. Note the large ventral horn cell with its extensive dendritic branching and axon (*A*) leaving the cord to become the motor fibre destined for a muscle. (Cajal, *Histologie du Système Nerveux*, reprinted ed., Madrid, 1952)

Ramón y Cajal (1852–1934) had embarked upon his studies of nerve cells using the Golgi method but applied to embryological material; he also developed the important reduced silver method. This led to fresh advance because in the embryo cells are sparse and so their ramification showed up lucidly without interference from branches of neighbouring cells: in addition the small preparations made it possible (as pointed out by Lorente de Nó) to see sections of individual organs in bird's-eye view as, for instance, the whole of the cerebellum or full cross-sections of the spinal cord (Fig. 2). Sherrington must have enjoyed looking at these pictures of neural organization. Here, ultimately, were the very facts he needed.

Is it too much to say of him [Sherrington wrote in 1949] that he is the greatest anatomist the nervous system has ever known? The subject had long been a favourite with some of the best investigators, previous to Cajal there were discoveries, discoveries which often left the physician more mystified than before, adding mystification without enlightenment. Cajal made it possible even for a tyro to recognize at a glance the direction taken by the nerve-current in the living cell, and in a whole chain of nerve cells.

He solved at a stroke the great question of the direction of the nerve-currents in their travel through brain and spinal cord. He showed, for instance, that each nerve-path is always a line of one-way traffic only, and that the direction of that traffic is at all times irreversibly the same. The so-called nerve-networks with unfixed direction of travel he swept away. The nerve-circuits are valved, he said, and he was able to point out where the valves lie, namely, where one nerve cell meets the next one.

The great Spaniard had a lively sense of the dramatic—a little out of fashion in European science of today—and in his autobiography made a momentous issue out of the meeting of the German Anatomical Society in 1889 (mentioned above) where he, then an unknown provincial, presented his slides to the leading histologists of the world. Even the critical von Kölliker was convinced. Cajal's reputation burst like a nova on the stellar firmament, never again to fade. The neurone theory had now found an indefatigable champion and this ardent defender of the faith immediately attracted the physiologists (and still does) because he always tried to explain his findings in functional terms. This imaginative trait in Cajal's writings made the

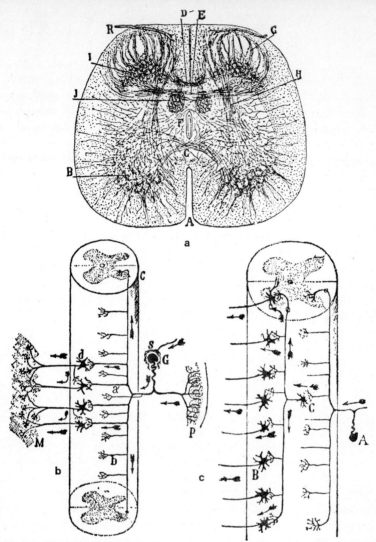

Fig. 2 (a) The collateral fibres shown in a cross-section of newly born dog's spinal cord, Golgi stain. (b) Diagram to show the passage of an impulse from a skin end-organ (*P*) to several ventral horn cells or motoneurones (*d*) which form end-plates on muscle fibres (*M*). Cajal has made this circuit monosynaptic, i.e. with one synaptic relay, but actually the monosynaptic circuit begins in muscular end-organs (see text). Note also the H-shaped grey matter of the cross-section and the spinal ganglion (*G*) which is on the straight route not provided with synapses. Cajal intended this figure to show the passage of action current in a unilateral circumscript reflex. (c) As (b), but showing merely afferent route (*A*) and efferent or motor route (*B*) of a diffuse reflex. By this term Cajal wanted to imply that the afferent input is spread through the intercalated cell or interneurone (*C*) to a very large number of ventral horn cells (*B*). The path is drawn disynaptic. A polysynaptic circuit would involve more than two interneurones. (Cajal, *Histologie du Système Nerveux*, reprinted ed., Madrid, 1952)

famous *Histologie du Système Nerveux* highly stimulating reading. It appeared in Spanish (a language Sherrington read in) 1897–1904, in French in 1909–1911 and was reprinted in 1952. It still continues to attract proselytes to the study of the central nervous system.

Cajal's work began with the retina, which in his old age he called his youth's tender passion. There, on a small scale, he first saw the types of cell and the pictures of organization which he later recovered higher up in the central nervous system. The retina he called 'a true nervous centre'. Well do I remember (speaking now as one of the 'proselytes') how this part of his work stimulated me to learn something about the central nervous system in Sherrington's laboratory in order to be able to investigate the retina as a true nervous centre.

Lorente de Nó, alongside de Castro one of Cajal's foremost disciples, once emphasized in conversation that his master, in taking up his stand so decisively in support of the contact notion, did not yet have definite evidence in its favour, having never seen the links of contact but only free endings. With the discovery of the actual contact points Cajal always and rightly credited Hans Held and Leopold Auerbach (the second). Held, working in His's laboratory in Leipzig, published his work in 1897, Auerbach in 1898. From then on the end-feet or *boutons terminaux*, by which the axon makes contact with the next cell or its dendrites became incorporated into Sherrington's ideas. In fact, in that very year (1897) and still unaware of Held's work, Sherrington, contributing to the new edition of Foster's *Textbook*, had written: 'So far as our present knowledge goes, we are led to think that the tip of a twig of the arborescence is not continuous with but merely in contact with the substance of the dendrite or cell-body on which it impinges. Such a special connexion of one nerve cell with another might be called a synapsis.' Today the most common technical term in use for the contact point is *synaptic knob*, when referring to the anatomical structure; it is abbreviated to *synapse* when speaking functionally or in more general terms.

In Stockholm, in 1906, Golgi and Cajal shared the Nobel prize 'in recognition of their work on the structure of the nervous system'. On that occasion each defended his own point of view. This clash of opinions is vividly related by Cajal in his auto-

Plate 1 Sir Charles Sherrington in his seventies, photographed in the
Old Physiology Laboratory at Oxford by Mr Bodle

Plate 2 Lord Adrian (left), Sir Charles Sherrington, and Professor Alexander Forbes at Ipswich on 5 June 1938. Sherrington, on being shown this photograph by Forbes, said: 'You and Adrian are having an argument and I—looking like the gargoyle that I am—am wondering who is right.' (By courtesy of Professor Forbes, Harvard)

biography. An eye-witness, the well-known physiologist Robert Tigerstedt, one time professor at the Royal Caroline Institute and later at Helsingfors in his native Finland, described the incident to me in 1922, taking a mischievous delight in pointing out that the learned antagonists had received the prize—which by the terms of the will must be awarded for a discovery—for two mutually exclusive discoveries. Actually both men had enough to their credit to deserve the reward and no one can read their prize lectures (published in *Les Prix Nobel* for 1906) without a feeling of respect for the objective criticism and intellectual honesty with which the two authors approached their subject.

Perhaps, since Sherrington leant so heavily upon Cajal's work, his personal impression of the Spanish master is worth putting on record: 'Cajal's rich voice compelled attention to whatever he said. The memory of that voice reminds me I have a privilege regarding him which, owing to lapse of time, must be becoming rare. My mind's eye recalls him as he walked and talked and indeed as his outward appearance was, just at that stage of his career when he had recently become, in his own line of science, an international figure. I see him a man perhaps a little below medium height—at least in London—broad-shouldered, spare and strongly built. Of dark complexion, his olive-skinned face lit by brilliant eyes deep brown in colour and of steady gaze. His hair almost black and closely cropped, trespassed low on a wide forehead. The strong face, completely shaven, had mobile, muscular lips. His hands as he sat and talked seemed to ask to be doing something' (1949).

Sherrington's greatest contribution to the physiology of the central nervous system was to supply the functional equivalents of the anatomical development that has now been briefly sketched. His experiments led up to the functional unit, his concepts centred around unitary behaviour of cells activated or inhibited at synapses, and his 'integrative action', as we shall see, is the knitting together of cells activated across synapses for a common goal. The present generation of experimentalists would, I believe, be willing to endorse this assessment of where Sherrington made a unique contribution to their field, and those who look backwards would also be prepared to admire the sagacity by which he went in for lines of approach that became sign-posts pointed towards the future.

4

Would Sherrington himself have thus placed the emphasis in his life's work? To judge by the foreword to the 1947 edition of his *Integrative Action*, the reply would have to be 'No'. This retrospective preface fully bears out his pupil Professor Denny-Brown's dictum that Sherrington was primarily a student of animal behaviour.

This may be so, but in the present era unitary analysis of nerve cells and their axons, pushed a second time to the frontier of research by Lord Adrian's work in the twenties and thirties, has given a richer harvest than any other approach to the physiology of the central nervous system. Also, it is not necessarily true that the individual worker is always a better judge of his own achievements than is posterity. The mind is a most secretive instrument, it integrates knowledge in its own way not knowing always why, or to what end, and never how. It has an inner developmental logic of its own and, time and again, future generations will interpret and reinterpret the traces it leaves on the pages of history if the mind concerned has been interesting enough and the individual sufficiently articulate to express his ideas. It is true that most steps in a piece of research can be motivated logically, but just why one problem is taken up rather than another often defies interpretation.

Sherrington, like most people who take a serious interest in the complexities of the central nervous system, must have been stimulated by a desire to explain organized behaviour, and to the end of his life continued to lay stress on reflexes as simplified items of behaviour in purposeful action. 'Reflex acts of the simple kind . . .' he said 'do not involve co-ordination of the highest and most delicate grades. For that reason they are likely to reveal explicitly some basal elements fundamental to all co-ordination. . . . Biologically the importance of a reflex is as an item of behaviour, hence biological study presents for each reflex the issue of its meaning as an animal act' (1932).

The literature on reflexes has an ancient history which begins with Leonardo da Vinci's observations on the behaviour of decapitated frogs. It includes Descartes' definition of reflexes as expressions of mechanical processes in his 'corporeal machinery', and continues with a large number of observations on frogs and other cold-blooded animals which were studied by experimenters in the early nineteenth century. (For the relevant literature

Liddell's monograph or Canguilhem's study *La Formation du concept de réflexe aux XVIIᵉ et XVIIIᵉ siècles*, may be consulted.) Towards the end of the last century many of the old authors were much excited by finding the decapitated frog scratching itself purposefully according to where a salt crystal was placed on its skin. From such observations they went off at a tangent into experiments and discussions for and against a 'Spinal Cord Soul' but this controversy did not survive the inevitable pruning of a subject that occurs with time.

Reflexology in the modern sense is founded on the discoveries embodied in the Bell-Magendie law, prior to which the common belief was that all nerves took their origin in the brain. Bell (1810) and Magendie (1822) laid the corner-stone for the insight that the ventral roots of the spinal cord are efferent or motor, the dorsal ones afferent or sensory. The final unequivocal proof was provided by Johannes Müller, who sectioned dorsal or ventral roots in frogs, in this way avoiding some of the complications encountered by Bell and Magendie who had used a mammalian preparation. This was objective fact, and it was taken up by the histologists who, by busily expanding knowledge about nerve cells and their interconnections, were the ones who during the latter half of the nineteenth century made the contributions that in the end liberated reflexology from the dead-weight of theology and psychology, and forced it to embark upon a course that ultimately made it a branch of natural science. As pure phenomenology the subject would soon have ceased to recruit good students.

The incessant wrangling which makes the phenomenological era of study of the central nervous system so exasperating to read and to review brings to mind Swift's—for his time apposite—description of science which, he says, 'is like a hen whose cackling one must notice because it might mean an egg'. At the time the 'eggs' were few, if Swift only alluded to scientific results capable of growing into something significant. There was first, von Helmholtz's pioneer measurement (1850) of conduction velocity in peripheral nerve, followed by similar measurements along the spinal columns where speed of conduction was found to slow down. His experiment once and for all time cleared away extravagant analogies with the velocity of the electrical current and made it necessary to think of nervous conduction in different terms. Reflex latent periods were measured repeatedly by a large number of authors and the results showed that events in the spinal cord required a finite and variable time during which something was evidently happening, or, in the picturesque language of Foster, the latent period is a 'busy time' for the spinal cord. To the same group of fundamental observations also belongs Du Bois-Reymond's discovery of the nerve's action-current which was a consequence of his improvement of the astatic galvanometer. Thus in the latter half of the nineteenth century it was definitely understood that the nervous message was likely to be an action-current travelling along the nerve at a finite velocity and setting up some intermediate process when it arrived via afferent fibres through dorsal roots into the spinal cord. On the ventral or efferent side it would again resume the character of an action-current and travel out to effector organs, muscles or glands.

The brunt of the fight for the establishment of the conceptual entity of a reflex as being some process in the spinal cord was borne by Marshall Hall in the 1830s. In the textbooks Sherrington would have read at Cambridge this matter was definitely settled. In fact, reflex action as a concept had been clearly understood by Johannes Müller.

Setchenow, one of Ludwig's pupils, had described both summation and central inhibition between 1863 and 1869. In a booklet dedicated to Ludwig (1863) Setchenow states that he used Türck's method. The frog, whose brain stem was sectioned anywhere between the quadrigeminal bodies and medulla oblongata, hung vertical with one foot dipping into weak sulphuric acid. Excitability increased after the operation so that the preparation pulled out its foot within a couple of seconds. This action could be greatly delayed by putting a salt crystal on the sectioned portion. The reflex time could also be much extended if the section went through the optic thalami which therefore were assumed to exercise a tonic inhibition released by lower sections. Instead of salt crystals electric stimulation could be used. Foster, in his *Textbook* (1879) had mentioned one of Setchenow's experiments in which the frog's foot-withdrawal reflex, elicited by sulphuric acid on its foot, could be inhibited by placing a salt crystal on its optic lobe. Similarly Foster's *Textbook* mentions that strong stimuli to any afferent nerves could retard or even wholly prevent reflex action. Several 'automatic centres' in the medulla were known; centres for respiration and vasomotor control, for instance. One knew that micturition and other spinal reflexes could be inhibited; this had been found in Goltz's laboratory (1874). Foster stated:

The spinal cord, and indeed the whole central nervous system, may be regarded as an intricate mechanism in which the direct effects of stimulation or automatic activity are modified and governed by the checks of inhibitory influences; but we have as yet much to learn before we can speak with certainty as to the exact manner in which inhibition is brought about. Seeing that in the ordinary actions of life the spinal cord is to a large extent a mere instrument of the cerebral hemispheres, we may readily expect that regulative inhibitory impulses passing from the latter to the former would be of frequent occurrence.

The Wallerian method, said Foster, is now being used for the study of the spinal cord 'with some striking results'. Among them were the findings of Türck and of Schiefferdecker, according to whom sections of the spinal cord gave degenerations below the cut in the lateral column and above it in the posterior columns. Flechsig with an embryological method had come to similar conclusions, all of which gave support to the work of Schiff and Brown-Séquard. Thus, in outline, the direction of travel of impulses in the white matter of the columns began to be known. William James had formulated a 'law of forward conduction' (1880), meaning that in neural systems conduction proceeds in one direction only, while in peripheral nerve the impulse travels both ways. Cajal reformulated this concept stating that the dendrites conducted towards the neurone and the axon away from it. Also it was known in a general way that the spinal cord consists of 'a series of cemented segments, having mutual relations one with the other, and all being governed by the dominant cerebral segments' (Foster).

An essential part of the physiology of the central nervous system is nowadays based on electrophysiology. This line of approach, starting from the original discoveries by Galvani and Volta, has developed in parallel with technical improvements of electrical equipment. Originally the subject was known as 'animal electricity'. The title of Du Bois-Reymond's classical monograph was in fact *Thierische Elektricität*. Abstracts of it had been translated into English in 1852. Du Bois-Reymond's great discovery of the nerve impulse or 'negative variation' (in his terminology) was therefore well known and a corner-stone in nerve physiology as taught in laboratories all over the world.

Matteucci had studied the muscle currents and Du Bois-Reymond had been the first to realize that polarization took place when voltaic current was passed through metal electrodes owing to differences in electrolytic composition between them and the tissue fluids. He had designed non-polarizable electrodes and with them found a 'current of rest' as well as polarization in excitable tissue. This work was continued by his disciple Pflüger who introduced the terms anelectrotonus and catelectrotonus for the polarization phenomena at anode and cathode respectively. However, Herrmann (1867) was the first to make sense of animal electricity, which had been some kind of mystical 'pre-existent force' until he showed that Du Bois-Reymond's current of rest really was an injury current. This signified that the inside of the tissue (unintentionally or intentionally injured) presented a potential difference with respect to the outside owing to its different electrolytic composition, and so current flowed between two non-polarizable electrodes joining inside with outside. This was the demarcation or injury current. The idea of a physiological membrane separating inside and outside of nerve and muscle cells, the two excitable tissues then, as now, in the focus of interest, arose from his discovery. It finally emerged in Bernstein's (1902) membrane theory of excitation in a form that made it accessible to experimental proof. Strictly speaking the existence of a nerve-cell membrane, capable of maintaining an ionic gradient between inside and outside, could not be proved to the hilt before the microelectrodes of the present day came to be used. Bernstein's theory was then found to embody a fundamental error (Hodgkin, A. F. Huxley) though correct in outline and definitely a step forward in the understanding of the electrical aspects of nervous excitation.

The electrophysiology Sherrington encountered in his undergraduate days was thus a science that was beginning to formulate its concepts and maintaining contact with developing electrochemistry. In animal physiology its problems centred around muscle and nerve and soon expanded to include retina

(Holmgren, 1865, Dewar and McKendrick, 1873) and the heart (Waller, Einthoven). When Sherrington decided in favour of nerve-cell contacts he refashioned thinking in this field along lines that determined its future course for all time and also tied it to the newly born science of electrophysiology, although his own approach never became electrophysiological. Only a contact theory could bridge the gap between reflex transmission and electrophysiology; such is the power of a fundamental concept like the synapse. Why not listen to Sherrington himself meandering in his slightly involved, visionary way about possibilities, some of which since have become realities? Thus in 1906:

> If the conductive element of the neurone be fluid, and if at the nexus between neurone and neurone there does not exist actual confluence of the conductive part of one cell with the conductive part of the other, e.g. if there is not actual continuity of physical phase between them, there must be a surface of separation. Even should a membrane visible to the microscope not appear, the mere fact of nonconfluence of the one with the other implies the existence of a surface of separation. Such a surface might restrain diffusion, bank up osmotic pressure, restrict the movement of ions, accumulate electric charges, support a double electric layer, alter in shape and surface-tension with changes in difference of potential, alter in difference of potential with changes in surface-tension or in shape, or intervene as a membrane between dilute solutions of electrolytes of different concentrations or colloidal suspensions with different signs of charge. It would be a mechanism where nervous conduction, especially if predominantly physical in nature, might have grafted upon it characters just such as those differentiating reflex-arc conduction from nerve-trunk conduction. For instance, change from reversibility of direction of conduction [as in peripheral nerve] to irreversibility might be referable to a membrane possessing irreciprocal permeability. . . .
> The characters distinguishing reflex-arc conduction from nerve-trunk conduction may therefore be largely due to intercellular barriers, delicate transverse membrane, in the former.
> In view, therefore, of the probable importance physiologically of this mode of nexus between neurone and neurone it is convenient to have a term for it. The term introduced has been *synapse.*' (*Integrative Action*, pp. 16–17.)

Later in the book he occasionally used the term *synaptic mem-*

brane. Today electron-microscopists have measured the distance between the two membranes of a single synaptic knob, one closing the end of the afferent terminal, the other belonging to the new cell. It forms a gap of 200 Å (0·0002 mm), the so-called synaptic cleft.

Sherrington, himself a behaviourist, was faced with the immense task of reshaping reflexology in such a fashion that the new ideas on synaptic contact could be worked into it. This meant taking a long view indeed and he came to spend a full life on realizing his programme. In the beginning the distance separating reflex phenomenology and concepts as precise as that of a synaptic membrane must have appeared to him wellnigh infinite.

Chapter 3

Sherrington's Basic Concepts

The gap between descriptive phenomenology and Sherrington's ideas about events at synaptic knobs had to be bridged by repeatable experiments which employed definite afferent nerves from sense organs for stimulation and likewise definite muscles for recording. Some familiarity with the details of the performing organization was necessary. Scanning the literature for knowledge of this type, elementary and at the same time systematic, the young Sherrington was bound to be disappointed. Merely in order to master the routine that is part of every successful advance in biology he himself had to collect the elementary information as to how muscles were innervated from the spinal cord and how sensory nerves entered the latter. Was the knee jerk, familiar to all physicians, really a reflex or some kind of muscular response? Which were the typical reflexes elicitable from the various nerves known from anatomy?

The young man of thirty who in 1887 became Lecturer in Systematic Physiology at St Thomas's Hospital in London and Fellow of his college at Cambridge may have had some general ideas about where his work in the end might lead him, but on the whole it seems more likely that he pinned his hopes to the rapidly advancing science of histology and wanted to perform experiments which made function interpretable in histological terms. In scientific matters Sherrington's optimism was unquenchable. I remember saying to him once (in 1932): 'I am sure there must be inhibition in the retina; after all, there is the "off-effect" when light is turned off, so strikingly like reflex rebound—and have we ever heard of a nervous centre without inhibition? But I cannot see how one ever shall be able to prove it.' Sherrington's reply was characteristic. 'Don't you worry. After a couple of years you will prove it yourself.' I left his office astonished and still sceptical. But he was right in this prophesy. Secretly he may well have reasoned in the same optimistic way about distant goals in reflexology.

Nevertheless, there he was with a future decided in general terms and the first thing he had to do was to improve his surgery, taking advantage of what one knew about asepsis and antiseptics after the discoveries of Pasteur, Koch and Lord Lister. The reflex work began with a 'Note on the knee jerk' in 1891 when Sherrington had been made Professor-Superintendent of the Brown Institute, a small Veterinary Charity with a laboratory attached. For some time he still kept one leg in the camp of bacteriology and with a young colleague (later, Sir) Armand Ruffer, started inoculating a horse with gradually increasing doses of a diphtheria culture. This was at a time when physicians in England were still sceptical of von Behring's work and that of the Institut Pasteur on diphtheria antitoxin. The story has often been told in print of how Sherrington saved the life of a nephew, a boy of eight, by going out to Lewes, where the family lived, and injecting him with his and Ruffer's antitoxin. This took place on a Sunday morning and the doctor in charge had already given up hope for the patient's recovery. Early in the afternoon the boy was clearly better and thence progress was uninterrupted. On Tuesday Sherrington returned to London, sought out Ruffer whose reaction was to go and tell Lord Lister immediately; so they went along but found the butler unwilling to let them in because his master had some Continental surgeons to dinner. The message they sent him back with proved to be a magic formula. Lord Lister asked the two young men in lounge-suits to join the formal dinner and they became the heroes of the evening. Thus ended the incident, as Sherrington told it to me, but in his written version in *Marginalia* the episode received a closing comment on Lord Lister: 'Unlike as he and Pasteur were in some ways, they both had as part of their inspiration an unshakeable confidence in the immense future before medicine.' Sherrington's own optimism had a similar basis.

St Thomas's offered the attraction of being Sherrington's first medical school where he went for some training in clinical medicine before he entered Cambridge University. It was the building we still know, opened by Queen Victoria in 1870, and facing the Houses of Parliament, but Sherrington's imagination went back to the Hospital's old traditions from the twelfth century in its ancient site near the Tabard Inn and opposite Southwark Cathedral from whence the pilgrims set out for Canterbury. Admirer of Keats that he was, he recalled that this was also the street in which the poet had written *To Homer*. Possibly he recalled:

> Aye on the shores of darkness there is light,
> And precipices show untrodden green,
> There is a budding morrow in midnight,
> There is a triple sight in blindness keen.

Gradually his work became what today we call neurophysiology. He had to demonstrate which muscles were physiological flexors and which were extensors, and to study the overlapping of both functions in some double-joint muscles. He was compelled to dissect and sever roots and stimulate both the central and the peripheral portion in order to elucidate in what manner ventral roots supplied flexors and extensors, how the incoming message from the dorsal roots distributed itself segmentally, and how these segments were laid out on body and limbs. His very good friend Henry Head was doing corresponding work on man by different methods (Head's zones, 1893). Sherrington had to find out where the afferents came from that gave typical reflex patterns. A reflex, after all, begins somewhere peripherally in a sense organ. Would only sense organs in the skin and in the joints and ligaments be concerned or would the muscles also contain sense organs? An Utrecht man, P. Q. Brondgeest (1860), had found neural tonus of reflex origin in frogs' hindlimbs after the skin had been removed, and Sherrington was inclined to accept his findings in spite of reports to the contrary by others. He therefore set out to prove by Wallerian degeneration (see pp. 27–8) that the mammalian muscle spindle of Weismann, Kühne, and Kölliker was a sense organ. Its nerve fibres did not survive removal of the spinal ganglions (dorsal root) and proved to be of very large diameter, maximally of the order of 20μ (1μ=one thousandth of a millimetre). These eventually turned out to be most important discoveries. In the same experiments he also showed that the Golgi-tendon organs were sensory endings.

In the course of those labours several individual problems rose to prominence, became formulated, and were solved. Others still remain with us very much in the shape he left them, or slightly clarified; his concepts also remain with us, in a different way as approaches to new problems, or as semi-automatic habits of thought. In about ten years Sherrington had advanced far enough to earn the international reputation which in 1903 gained him the invitation to deliver the Silliman Lectures at Yale University (1904), published as *The Integrative Action of the Nervous System* (1906), the famous classic containing the essence of the new approach to the nervous system and a scholarly appreciation of contemporary work. The task gave him some anxiety. To Harvey Cushing he wrote in February 1904: 'Mais il faut de l'audace, et encore de l'audace et toujours de l'audace!' Perhaps he had his misgivings about the students. According to John Fulton the large audience had dwindled to four people at the last lecture, but he was personally very popular at Yale and the book made up for everything. The Yale view of it, as stated by the well-known physiologist, Professor Russell H. Chittenden, chairman of the Silliman Committee (1903–1922) was: 'Sherrington's book embodying these lectures, brought more credit to the university than any of the other books of the series' (letter to John Fulton, March 16, 1935). It is still maintained on the list of publications from the Yale University Press and was also reprinted in England in 1947 at the time of the International Congress of Physiology at Oxford.

In presenting Sherrington's work I shall take a few examples from his fundamental experiments, explain his concepts, and show how they led to fresh problems, many of which have subsequently been solved in other laboratories. These lines of development will be followed up to the present. This mode of presentation will place chronology a little in abeyance—no more than is done in modern novels and for the same purpose— because the timeless component of Sherrington's achievements is in the centre of interest here. Certainly in his old age Sherrington himself did not think the biographical element of a scientist's life significant enough to be worth recording, except in outlines in an obituary. He held it to be uneventful and lacking in general appeal, compared with the lives of, say, statesmen and soldiers. Sherrington, like many other intellectuals, may

SYLLABUS	PROTOCOLS
*	*
Gastronomic Experiments	SOME OF NATURE'S FIRST EXPERIMENTS WITH THE SYNAPTIC SYSTEM
FOR THE DEVELOPMENT OF	ON THE HALF SHELL
An International Synaptic System	
	APPLICATIONS OF CARMINE STAINING FLUID
INTEGRATING	WITH A SPOON
Certain Newly Medulated Neurons	
	ULTRAMARINE BRAIN FOOD STARVATON ARMY STAPLE
WITH	
THE HIGHER CENTER,	METAMERES OF SKELETAL MUSCULATURE FROM A HIGHER VERTEBRATE
PROFESSOR C. S. SHERRINGTON, M.D., LL.D., F.R.S.	
SILLIMAN LECTURER	DECEREBRATED SQUAB EXHIBITING TOASTOTROPISM
Accompanied by	VERDANT PROPRIONOCICEPTOR ALLEVIATOR
EXPLOSIONS FROM BROCA'S CONVOLUTION by the	PROTEID SECRETION OF HYPERTROPHIED SEBACEOUS GLANDS
BIOLOGICAL QUARTET	
Concluded by	MICROTOME SECTIONS BY FREEZING PROCESS
DEMONSTRATIONS BY PROFESSOR MENDEL ON VARIOUS HUMAN SUBJECTS	SACCHARINE STIMULI OF TRIGEMINUS
SCRATCH REFLEX KNEE JERK SHIVERING SPINAL SHOCK	
	CAFFEINE FOR
Summary of Results PROFESSOR SHERRINGTON	VASO-MOTOR REACTIONS

Fig. 3 Sample of Yale academic humour, 1904 vintage. The menu of the Silliman dinner

have had secret dreams of a life of action, especially when attacked by accidie (*acedia*), the '*melancholiae species quae Monachorum propria est*' and which comes '*e nimia lectione*' and produces '*taedium cordis*' and '*languor spiriti*' (Ducange). Rumour has it that once in the company of friends, when everybody stated what they would have preferred to be, Sherrington said: 'An admiral.' Would this have been to him an eventful life worth recording? I can remember Sherrington praising Virginia Woolf's two masterpieces, *The Waves* and *To the Lighthouse*, both extreme specimens of life without will and action, and so, perhaps, one looks in vain for consistent patterns within the 'subliminal fringes' of emotions that surround scientific activity.

There is some evidence that Sherrington himself thought the results on reciprocal innervation the most important he ever obtained. These are often misrepresented to signify that whenever flexor muscles contract, extensor muscles must relax, and vice versa. The principle of reciprocal innervation means in the first instance merely that such a mechanism exists; it had, in fact, been observed before Sherrington made something out of it by systematic analysis. Then secondly under what conditions the mechanism is operative and to what extent it can be overridden by central control (even commonsense tells us that we can maintain flexors and extensors simultaneously activated), and whether it is symmetrical with respect to flexors and extensors. Technically this work culminated in Sherrington's demonstration of reciprocal innervation of antagonistic eye muscles. This was perhaps the time when he went to 'Dew' (A. G. Dew-Smith), a wealthy amateur scientist, founder of the Cambridge Scientific Instrument Co., pupil and friend of Foster—'always dressed in a velvet jacket' (Sherrington)— who took pleasure in making instruments for the young physiologists, and asked whether he could provide him with some light levers of aluminium for recording the movements of these tiny muscles. 'Have you ever thought of a straw?' said Dew-Smith. Those were happy days! Now he would have had to ask for a grant to buy a valve with a movable anode and start building a circuit of expensive parts for recording those same contractions greatly amplified for the screen of a cathode ray tube.

Denny-Brown—in agreement with his master, as I imagine—
is inclined to think that Sherrington's 'outstanding single
achievement was the measurement, charting, and analysis of
spinal inhibition, and the innate pattern of reciprocal innervation. It is hard now to realize the great difficulty at the beginning of establishing that inhibition is an *active* process, and not
mere absence of activity. That this was also his own pride,'
Denny-Brown continues, 'was shown by his shyly giving me
Hamburger's statement about him that is printed at the front
of the *Selected Writings* (edited by Denny-Brown, 1939). It
reads in free translation, "Those who took part in Sherrington's
demonstration at the International Congress in Cambridge in
1898, who felt the triceps of the monkey melt under their
fingers so to speak at the moment the biceps contracted, have
permanently enriched their fund of knowledge."'

This observation implies that in actual work with reciprocal
reflexes, the experimenter must be able to isolate mechanically
the two muscles around the same joint and then connect their
freed tendons to myographs for the recording of contractions and
relaxations. This procedure was an essential step in Sherrington's
advance to clarity, along with denervation of unwanted muscles.
At that time myographs had been chiefly used for recording the
contractions in the isolated nerve-muscle preparation of the frog.
Sherrington made myographic recording a regular feature of his
procedure and started measuring reflex effects in terms of contraction and relaxation. Thus every experiment left actual
tracings to consider afterwards. Another technical advance was
the use of the induced current (then called 'faradic') for repetitive
stimulation of bared nerves instead of the voltaic (mostly called
'galvanic') currents generally employed. Repetitive shocks
from induction coils had been used, for instance, by Ferrier
(1881) for stimulating the surface of the brain and this technical
improvement had made it possible for him to advance beyond the
pioneer work of Fritsch and Hitzig (1870), carried out in the
latter's home, according to legend, on his wife's dressing-table
(Liddell). The voltaic battery caused a twitch only, one on
closing the circuit, another on opening it, while the hammer of
the induction coil kept stimulation going repetitively. In his
obituary of Ferrier, Sherrington underlined this technical
improvement and so must have been struck by its importance.

The myographs in those days were isotonic, meaning that shortening of the muscle in contraction was allowed to take place. The movement was transferred to a lever writing on a rotating drum, lightly sooted. When the muscle shortens in contraction or lengthens in relaxation change of tone or, more correctly, tension is negligible, hence *iso*-tonic. If shortening is prevented, tension rises. Recording is called isometric (constant length). This is the more satisfactory technique of the two, and after the First World War it was the one used exclusively in Sherrington's laboratory.

Inhibition had to be measured by relaxation, but this presupposed that the motor cells initially were in a state of excitation, and so, for precise work, a preparation was necessary in which either of the two antagonistic muscles was contracted from the beginning while the other one was made to contract by tetanic (repetitive) stimulation. Sherrington's great opportunity for developing in parallel the two problems of inhibition and reciprocal innervation came when he re-discovered the decerebrate preparation and quickly realized how it could be used. This was in 1896, just after he had taken over the Holt chair of Physiology at Liverpool (1895); his predecessor there, Francis Gotch, having beaten him in competing for the succession at Oxford.

The full report on decerebrate rigidity came in 1898. Under deep chloroform anaesthesia the cartotid arteries were tied, the vertebral circulation manually compressed behind the neck, the brain stem sectioned (between the *corpora quadrigemina*) and the brain in front of it removed. There ensued a curious state of extensor rigidity and, of course, profound unconsciousness. Sherrington used to refer to this state as 'exaggerated standing' but his technical term remained 'decerebrate rigidity'. It is seen in mammals including man (on rare occasions born in this condition). Sherrington's favourite preparation for reflex work thereafter became the decerebrate cat, unconscious and with extensor muscles stiffened in permanent contraction, useful as a reflex animal for hours after the effects of anaesthesia had worn off (Fig. 4).

Sherrington wrote at the time (1898): 'The condition is one possessing considerable physiological interest, but I have not succeeded in finding any description of it prior to the above

Plate 3   C. S. Roy and C. S. Sherrington at the door of the Old Pathology Laboratory, Cambridge 1893. Photograph by Dr Louis Cobbett, working in Roy's laboratory at the time. (By courtesy of Professor, Sir Bryan Matthews, Cambridge)

Plate 4 Harvey Cushing and Sherrington, probably at Harvard in 1927.
(By courtesy of Professor Wilder Penfield, Montreal)

mentioned' (his own). This was a mistake. Though unnamed, decerebrate rigidity had been seen by Magendie, Flourens, Claude Bernard, and Vulpian. Liddell quotes a very good description of it in the rabbit by Magendie (1823). Therefore, when Sherrington entered, all the ingredients of the synthesis he made out of the three components, inhibition, reciprocal innervation and decerebrate rigidity, were there, pre-existent as crude forms of discovery, of the kind which in the nineteenth century were often called 'phenomena'. They were ready for someone to make them stepping-stones on the road towards

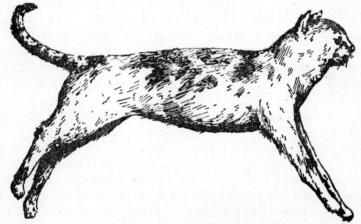

Fig. 4 Decerebrate rigidity according to Pollock and Davis. This is actually caused by anaemic decerebration of large parts of the cerebellum and the brain-stem below the intercollicular section used by Sherrington, but superficially the two forms of rigidity look alike. (from fig. 4, L. J. Pollock and L. Davis, *J. Comp. Neur.*, 1930, *50*, 384)

the understanding of something. The fresh mind of Sherrington was hot on the scent of what could be done. First of all, he had to succeed in making the decerebrate preparation survive long enough at a reasonably good blood pressure. Only under these circumstances could the advantage of a spinal cord, undamped by anaesthesia, and therefore capable of revealing important secrets, be fully exploited. The operation was developed and perfected until this became possible, and then Sherrington had available for analysis a background of excitatory state (in the ventral horn cells of extensors) against which inhibition could be measured.

5

It is no exaggeration to state that if Sherrington had done nothing except introduce decerebrate rigidity for the detailed analysis of inhibition, he would be remembered for having created and made use of an approach that ultimately paved the way for an understanding of how neurones are actively silenced.

With inhibition, as with excitation—which are two fundamental modes of action of nerve cells—there are always two different primary questions: (1) what can we learn about the process itself, its physico-chemical nature, and (2) the integrative point of view, how is the process made use of in a specific context, for instance, in an organized pattern of behaviour? The latter question often touches teleology and so runs the risk of becoming an anthropomorphic analysis of 'purpose', as in the old discussion of the Spinal Cord Soul. Most physiologists shirk thinking in terms of 'purpose' but there is some truth in what von Brücke (the elder) said, that teleology is like the kind of woman people do not want to be seen with in the street, yet are prepared to tender their love to in secret.

In *The Integrative Action of the Nervous System* Sherrington stated sensibly that the whole idea of adaptation under natural selection which has meant so much for morphology was on the point of beginning to influence physiology. 'Pure reflexes are admirably adapted to certain ends. They are reactions which have long proved advantageous in the phylum . . .' And he concluded: 'The purpose of a reflex seems as legitimate and urgent an object for natural inquiry as the purpose of the colouring of an insect or a blossom.' Nor did he hesitate to discuss at some length the purpose of reciprocal innervation.

At the present time teleology is stealthily creeping in by the back-door. Engineers have started to look for physiological models of man-made machines which employ servo-mechanisms and are thus explicitly designed with a definite purpose in view, say, to run a motor at constant speed or to maintain a constant temperature, not to mention James Watt's invention of the fly-wheel for the steam engine. Therefore the cautious rebels of today who want to experiment along such lines within the framework of physiology are perfectly safe and perhaps even respected by their critical colleagues as long as they use servo-terminology, just as Claude Bernard was safe in the last century, when he spoke of mechanisms designed to maintain the constancy of the internal milieu. For this concept the American physiologist Walter Cannon coined the term 'homeostasis' in the present century.

The principle of reciprocal innervation is an example of the second or integrative point of view in which inhibition is given

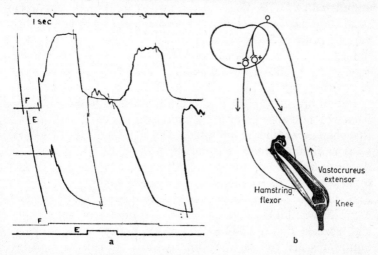

Fig. 5 (a) Decerebrate cat. Reciprocal effects of antagonistic muscles of the knee: (*F*) flexor of knee, *semitendinosus*; (*E*) extensor of knee, *vastocrureus*. Of the signal lines (below), the upper (*F*) marks by its rise the period of stimulation of the ipsilateral peroneal nerve; the lower marks similarly the stimulation of the contralateral peroneal nerve. (Sherrington, *Quart. J. exp. Physiol.*, 1913, 6, 251) (b) Diagram of cross-section of spinal cord to illustrate innervation of knee extensor and knee flexor by simplest possible circuit, explaining reciprocal effects of ipsilateral muscular origin, excitatory (+) for extensor and inhibitory (−) for flexor motoneurone. The same extensor muscular afferent has terminals on both types of motoneurone

a rôle in organized activity. Fig. 5 shows an experiment (1908) with the decerebrate animal. There are two muscles, the knee flexor *semitendinosus* (F) and its extensor antagonist *vasto-crureus* (E) attached to isotonic myographs. The extensor is contracted in decerebrate rigidity. Flexor stimulation from an afferent nerve is started at F, as indicated by the marker below the myographic responses, and maintained without interruption also during the brief extensor stimulation at E (signal). No sooner is stimulation of the afferent nerve begun at F than it elicits a flexor contraction concomitant with an extensor relaxation by inhibition. The afferent nerve is on the *ipsilateral* side (same side as the responding muscle) and the reflex is known as the ipsilateral flexion reflex. From the contralateral side it is easier to obtain a crossed extensor reflex. When this side is stimulated at E, the flexor is relaxed by inhibition. This reciprocal organization in the spinal cord apparently is accessible to various reflexes and central commands. An enumeration of the different sites from which reciprocal effects could be obtained was given by Sherrington and H. E. Hering (son of Ewald Hering) in 1897.

Inhibition as a *peripheral* process was well known at the time from the famous observation by the brothers Weber (1845) that the heart could be inhibited, even to a temporary standstill, by stimulation of the vagus nerve. Biedermann (1888) had also discovered that there was an inhibitory nerve to the claw muscle of the crayfish. Such examples of peripheral inhibition were mentioned in *The Integrative Action*. It has taken us half a century of experimentation to come back to Sherrington's original models and realize that fundamentally both central and peripheral inhibitions are run on the same pattern, as will be explained later. At the end of the last century Biedermann's discovery sent Sherrington on a chase for peripheral inhibition in the muscles of mammals. He had to establish by experimentation that such a mechanism did not exist in vertebrates. In them motor control is organized by *central* inhibition alone.

The simplest scheme one can imagine for the reciprocal reflex, illustrated in Fig. 5, is shown on the right in the same figure. There is an afferent nerve from a sense organ. In the spinal cord it sends one branch to form excitatory synapses on a flexor ventral horn cell, another has inhibitory synapses on an extensor cell. Each cell transmits the message to an efferent nerve that has motor end-plates (which again are synapses) on a number of muscle fibres. For a motor cell in the ventral horn *plus* the muscle fibres (around a hundred) which its terminal branches innervate Sherrington (1925) introduced the term *motoneurone*. Its peripheral nerve-muscle portion is mostly referred to as a *motor unit* (Fig. 6). This concept proved to be very useful, not least in medicine, because it brought 'unitary' thinking in reflexology to a level of clarity that required but little knowledge of special physiology to be understood.

More complex schemes than that of Fig. 5 can be imagined in which one or several intercalated cells, so called internuncials or *interneurones*, are inserted in the spinal path. In studying the scratch reflex Sherrington introduced the term *disynaptic* (1906) for one spinal interneurone, meaning two synaptic relays, the first by the afferent nerve on an interneurone, the second by the

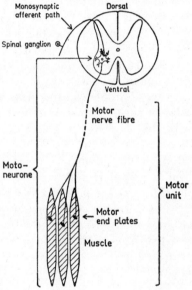

Fig. 6 Diagrammatic illustration of the concepts 'motoneurone' and 'motor unit'

interneurone on the motoneurone. At the time he used to think that the simplest reflex pathway was disynaptic, yet did not include interneurones in his diagrams. The scratch reflex which he called disynaptic is more likely to be polysynaptic.

Simple as it is, the diagram of Fig. 5 shows the increase in precision that synaptic thinking gave to problems of central excitation and inhibition, as shown in the reflexes of the spinal cord. Thus it postulates specific inhibitory and excitatory terminals. 'In denoting one set of central terminations of an afferent arc *specifically inhibitory*, it is here meant,' said Sherrington, 'that by no mere change in intensity or mode of stimulation can they be brought to yield any other effect than inhibition,' a daring statement in 1906. It practically amounts to postulating inhibitory synapses and the word 'terminations' is used merely because it avoids specifying whether the inhibitory effect is at the ending or at the motoneurone side of the point of contact. One more consequence was that if the velocities of conduction of the incoming and outgoing volley of action currents could be measured across a monosynaptic path, then synaptic delay could be estimated and thereafter one could begin formulating ideas as to the mechanism of synaptic transmission itself. Vice versa also, if the minimal synaptic delay across one synaptic interface in the spinal cord were known, one could use this figure for the purpose of labelling a given transmitted event as monosynaptic.

One approach to these problems came from the study of the knee jerk whose latent period was so brief that its reflex nature was open to doubt. By showing the extensor knee jerk to be inhibitable by flexor nerve stimulation in the manner just described, Sherrington (1892) supplied crucial evidence for its reflex nature. The late Paul Hoffman (who had worked with Sherrington just before the First World War) concluded at an early stage (1919–22), from accurate measurements on man, that the knee jerk was the *monosynaptic* reflex whose existence had to be postulated from Cajal's pictures, in which some afferent fibres contacted ipsilateral motoneurones. At the time, however, the conduction velocity of mammalian nerve was unknown.

At about this time the vacuum tube entered physiology and with it the possibility of amplifying small electrical events without distortion and delay. The cathode ray oscillograph was introduced by Gasser and Erlanger in 1922. All earlier recording instruments, from the capillary electrometer of Lippmann (1871) to the string galvanometer of Einthoven (1901) had been compromises which in different degree sacrificed speed of recording to sensitivity, but here, at last, was a fast enough recording instrument with its low sensitivity made negligible by amplification. Gone were the elaborate calculations and approximations which had been needed with an instrument even as fast as the capillary electrometer, in order to derive the true form of the action current from the photographed movements of the shadow of a mercury disc. One proper field of application for the new instrument was, of course, the action current of nerve, now recorded as an action potential across the grid of a vacuum tube. The classical papers of Gasser and Erlanger and their co-workers at St Louis solved the problem of conduction velocity of the nervous impulse by the technique of leading off at different points along the nerve. Conduction velocity was found to be proportional to fibre diameter. The largest muscular afferents had already been seen by Sherrington to possess cross-section diameters of the order of 20μ. This, with the average proportionality coefficient of 6·0, makes them conduct at 120 metres per second. Hoffmann and Keller in 1928 were therefore on reasonably firm ground when they reasserted that the brief stretch reflex, which we call the knee jerk, was monosynaptic with a transmission time of the order of 1·0 millisecond (msec.). Yet they were cautious enough to present this conclusion as an hypothesis.

The earliest precise measurements of minimal synaptic delay of motoneurones came from experiments in which conduction velocity could be neglected. In 1935–39 Lorente de Nó inserted stimulating and recording microelectrodes into the nucleus of the oculomotor neurones and, using single shocks, recorded direct and indirect electrical responses, the latter having been transmitted across one synaptic relay. The minimal delay was found to be of the order of 0·5 msec., a good average figure being 1·0 msec. A few years later the knee jerk itself was tested by David Lloyd (1943) at the Rockefeller Institute. Brief stretch was applied by a magnetic device (supplanting the tendon tap) and conduction velocities measured. In full agreement with previous work, the monosynaptic nature of the phasic stretch reflexes (knee jerk, ankle jerk, etc.) was now definitely established.

What Foster had called the 'busy time' of the spinal cord had thus by the logic, not to say the magic, of synaptic thinking been split up into brief, explosive events at mono-, di-, or poly-synaptic relays separated by intervals for conduction along intraspinal fibres and terminals. This was a concept capable of further development; at the moment it is sufficient to have shown for one specific case how Sherrington's conceptions led to the formulation of precise problems and experiments. Undoubtedly this development would have been greatly delayed if he had chosen to interpret his data in terms of a protoplasmic continuum.

Returning again to the last century, one can show how another line of purely integrative work dealing with reflex patterns also led in the end to the formulation of definite synaptic problems. This is worth emphasizing because today there is quite a gap between the people interested in nervous transmission and those trying to understand how the organism makes use of transmitted messages and the properties of neural networks. The integrative approach has attracted relatively few of Sherrington's former disciples in this age, transmission at synapses being in the centre of interest. But among his early co-workers T. Graham Brown, Professor of Physiology at Cardiff, contributed valuable papers on problems of this type (co-ordination of movement, stepping, reciprocal innervation); another, the late Rudolf Magnus, Professor of Pharmacology at Utrecht, a German by birth, studied postural and righting reflexes, elicited by natural stimuli, in particular from the vestibular organs and the neck; in this he was also inspired by Ewald's work on the labyrinth. Magnus brought this field to a high level of perfection and his monograph *Die Körperstellung* (1924) remains a classic in reflexology. These problems are bound to reappear on the stage.

Magnus had worked with Sherrington at Liverpool in 1908: he was there when he received the telegram that invited him to the chair at Utrecht. Sherrington had met Ewald in Goltz's laboratory at Strasbourg where he was second in command at the time. Important studies on the spinal animal were performed in Goltz's laboratory in the nineties and Sherrington visited it several times.

The work described now was begun at Liverpool during an era which in many ways was the most productive in Sherrington's scientific life; a great deal of experimental work was on the programme, so much in fact, that *Integrative Action* supplied a necessary summary together with conclusive evidence that Sherrington's work during this eruptive period was sustained by leading ideas. These emerge matured in the *Selected Writings* (1939), which was thoughtfully compiled and commented on by Denny-Brown, who made an organized whole

out of the writings originating in Sherrington's nimble mind—
this mind which in such a curious way combined attention to
detail and criticism with artistic spontaneity. The central
nervous system was really a fitting subject for it.

Out of the extensive work on reciprocal innervation grew
studies on two known reflex patterns, the ipsilateral flexion
reflex and the crossed extensor reflex (Freusberg, 1874, in
Goltz's laboratory). These were found to be connected and both
were dependent on painful stimuli, in particular to the skin, to

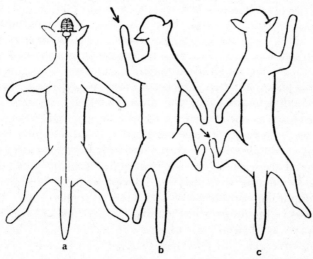

Fig. 7   The reflex figures illustrated above are positions in decerebrate
rigidity. (a) initial state; (b) stimulation of left fore-foot; (c) stimulation
of left hind-foot. (Sherrington, *J. Physiol.*, 1898, *12*, 319)

which the ipsilateral limb reacted with flexion and the contralateral limb with extension, the two movements together forming one of the many reflex 'figures' that Sherrington described
(Fig. 7). An ipsilateral flexor reflex could also be elicited by
stimulating purely muscular afferents from end-organs sensitive
to stretch, especially in the spinal animal, and this was reciprocally connected with inhibition of the extensor which opposed it
and was thus the other half of the circuit shown in the diagram
of Fig. 5, sense organs in extensors and flexors both exciting
their own muscle and inhibiting the antagonist. Both excitatory
reflexes were found by Lloyd to be monosynaptic.

In the development of Sherrington's ideas on interaction, antagonism, excitation, and inhibition, there were three reflexes which proved to be of greatest importance. These were the ipsilateral flexor, the crossed extensor, and the stretch reflex, of which the tendon jerk was one. At the time Sherrington himself, student of behaviour that he was, may well have been more interested in the scratch reflex and the various reflex figures or attitudes which the decerebrate animal assumed in response to different types of stimuli. These involved crossed reciprocal patterns and the combined action of 'long' and 'short' spinal paths (Sherrington and Laslett); this was continued in some admirable work by Magnus and described in *Körperstellung*. But any appraisal of Sherrington from perspectives valid today must throw the emphasis differently and start with the three reflexes just mentioned. The reason for this is that they became instrumental in advancing the theory while the scratch reflex, for instance, as such the work of an experimental perfectionist and complete in itself, has remained a beautiful thing on the shelf, too complex for the terms in which we think, struggling as we still are with the development of first principles. Some day it may be possible to go beyond description and devise methods for simplifying problems of this more complex type. Those scientists of the future will then find in Sherrington's paper, the anacrusis, as it were, for the new piece of music that they expect to create. Insight has married experimental skill in Sherrington's best papers and so they will always repay reading.

Initially, Sherrington was surprised to find that such a large number of limb nerves, which always contain a mixture of inhibitory and excitatory afferents, monotonously elicited the ipsilateral flexion reflex. Later he discovered several exceptions, among them the reflex that he named the 'extensor thrust' (1899), neglected by analysts of today. But from the early observations he drew the obvious conclusion that a limited number of flexor motoneurones was accessible to a very large number of afferent terminals which had arrived from different peripheral nerves across interneurones. This, in synaptic terms, is *convergence* towards a *final common path*, in this particular case the motoneurone. Anatomical convergence is illustrated in Fig. 8. With the improved staining methods of today one would expect to find a reflex with a *receptive field* as wide as that of the flexor reflex to impinge upon its motoneurones with a very large number of synaptic knobs, and this also is the case.

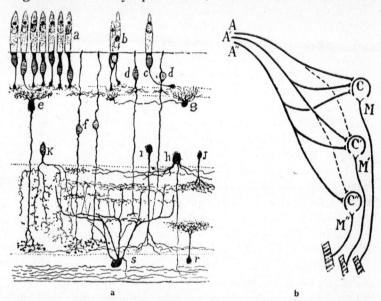

a   b

Fig. 8   (a) Transverse section of the retina of a lizard, Golgi stain. Note, on the left, that the receptors *a* converge towards the bipolar cell *e* whose end-plates branch in the layer of the ganglion cells. Only one ganglion cell *s* was stained but its widely branching dendrites must obviously be converged upon by the branches of many bipolar cells. The horizontal cell *g* is an interneurone which joins the end-feet of distant receptors to one another. These were the pictures that inspired Cajal to go on with his work and study the organization of the rest of the central nervous system. Of this, the retina is an outlying portion. (Cajal, *Histologie du Système Nerveux*, reprinted ed., Madrid, 1952) (b) Diagram of convergence on three motoneurones *C* in the spinal cord. The three nerves *A* send terminal branches to the different motoneurones, and the unbroken lines indicate greater synaptic density than the broken ones. Synaptic density will serve to grade the effect of a shock to afferents *A* and hence the outcome in terms of gram-isometric contraction in the parallel muscles fibres *M*. (Sherrington, *Proc. Roy. Soc.*, 1925, *B97*, 519)

Synaptic convergence then became for Sherrington the basis of interaction.

Although at an early stage Sherrington had visualized both the synapses as valves making reflex conduction irreversible, and the convergence of terminals with synapses, either excitatory or inhibitory, as the basis for interaction, he was loath at that stage to carry interpretation too far. In *Integrative Action* this part of his teaching is still given in very general terms. Also, one knew too little about the nervous message from sense organs to go further. But, as we shall see, there was a great deal of latent power in the synaptic approach that could be released by slight technical improvements and some advance in the understanding of the afferent message. To begin with, Sherrington pointed out that temporal summation was a characteristic feature of trans-synaptic conduction suggesting the existence of an excitatory remainder after the first impulse. Thus synaptic action was different from the all-or-nothing type of response of peripheral nerve. Spatial summation would be a consequence of convergence of excitatory paths from different sources on to the common final path. An excitatory remainder was indicated also by the so-called reflex after-discharge, excitation continuing for a while after cessation of electrical stimulation, which was seen with many types of reflexes.

For further conceptual developments based essentially on muscle alone as indicator of the central states which Sherrington wanted to study, the isotonic recording had its defects. Muscle is a machine which in response to a given stimulus such as the efferent (outgoing) impulse or impulses produces active tension, but the amount of tension it delivers depends upon its length, increasing up to a point when the muscle is extended, decreasing again when the muscle is pulled out to greater lengths. In order to avoid such variations, length is held constant (barring some yielding in the tendon) and then the natural expression of the amount of reflex activity is the isometrically recorded tension in grams. Also, rise of tension precedes shortening and therefore is a faster indicator of activity than the change in length. The relation between efferent activity and isometric tension of the muscle would depend upon the all-or-none law, which in the first decades of this century was subjected to careful scrutiny by several workers and generally found to be accurate (Keith Lucas, Adrian, Forbes, Pratt, and Eisenberger). Provided that efferent excitation is constant, individual motor units therefore always deliver the tension they are capable of producing under the defined circumstances.

Consider first the case of a weak single shock direct to the efferent motor nerve. The measured tension in the stimulated muscle will be the constant all-or-none response of a certain number of motor units. A stronger shock (by activating additional fibres) would excite more motor units and on the all-or-none law each motor unit would add its tension value to the total, provided the direction of pull of the fibres on the myograph were the same. A maximum shock would mobilize all nerve fibres and give the maximum tension which is divisible into the fractional tensions delivered by each motor unit. The amount of tension would be greater for a constant tetanus to the nerve, because it is then summated by the muscle fibres, but otherwise the behaviour of the muscle machine would be additively all-or-none, as with single shocks. This reasoning presupposes that each nerve fibre has its own muscle fibres (which is the definition of the motor unit), meaning that individual nerve fibres should not overlap on the same muscle fibres. If they did, the effect of one nerve fibre might add to or occlude that of another, and so the theoretical basis for additive partial tensions would be non-existent. Claims to the effect that a great deal of overlap of innervation exists in the limb muscles that were used by the Sherrington school have been published, even quite recently (Hunt and Kuffler, 1954), but they have always been refuted (cf. Brown and Matthews, 1960).

The essential trouble that Sherrington faced in attempting to develop a quantitative reflexology in terms of additive isometric tensions of active motor units lay not so much in the factors discussed as in the nature of the reflex discharge itself. Ultimately also his torsion wire myographs became sufficiently fast to record muscle contractions correctly. But since practically all reflexes proved to be bursts of impulses or tetani (only the knee jerk approached in synchrony the twitch caused by a single shock) were these tetani really constant in frequency of discharge? Possibly when they were fused (as they tended to be), but behind a seemingly fused muscular response there might have been unfused asynchronous discharges. The string galvanometer, by recording muscular action currents, gave some help and so did the comparison with a maximal tetanus to the motor nerve, which could always be produced as a control of reflex tension. Threshold effects and maximal contractions also proved to be useful limiting conditions in analytical work; and for the rest, when after the First World War Sherrington took to isometric myography, with his thirty years of experience he could steer a safe course between hidden rocks. We shall see how the method was used to release some of the latent power of the synaptic approach and set the stage for the next act. The results were finally summarized in *Reflex Activity of the Spinal Cord* (1932) which Sherrington wrote together with his co-workers, Stephen Creed, Derek Denny-Brown, J. C. Eccles, and E. G. T. Liddell, who had a large share in the success of his endeavours. By this time Adrian's major discoveries (from 1925 onwards) were common knowledge, and with them a change of scenery gradually took place, but that is a later story.

Actually Sherrington's own views were fully developed by 1925 when he wrote a theoretical paper for the Proceedings of the Royal Society, *Remarks on Some Aspects of Reflex Inhibition*. This began with excitation, and went on to discuss inhibition; much of the experimental work that followed consisted in testing and developing views enunciated in that paper. I know that Sherrington himself was quite excited about the combination of isometric myography with the all-or-none law, in which the string galvanometer supplemented this knowledge with an overall picture of the action currents from the muscle. The latter record is commonly called the electromyogram. It showed how long the nervous discharge lasted and also the moment when inhibition set in, being a little faster than the myogram.

The various consequences of *synaptic convergence* (defined above) as well as the temporal course of reflexes became the most important frontiers of attack. 'Over and over again in the arrangement of the conducting paths of the nervous system there are places where two or more such paths converge and run to one. There two or more of the convergent paths when active will interact' (Ferrier Lecture, 1929). Assume, for instance, that each of four separate afferents or sensory nerves, A, B, C, and D elicit maximal reflexes of the order of 1,500, 1,000, 800, and 600 gram tension respectively. The sum of them is 3,900 g. while the muscle chosen, for instance soleus, an ankle extensor, could only respond with 2,230 g. when tetanized maximally and directly through its own motor nerve. Clearly therefore the afferents A-D for this crossed extensor reflex had converged towards the same motoneurones of the *pool* of that muscle to engage the same final common paths. The ipsilateral flexor reflex, as mentioned above, could be mobilized from so many nerves that the sum tension they gave enormously exceeded the maximum tetanic tension of any of the flexors stimulated directly through its motor nerve. Convergence is schematically illustrated in Fig. 8.

For another aspect of convergence Denny-Brown and Sherrington (1928) used two afferents such as A and B of Fig. 9, and the flexor reflex in the spinal animal. Assume that A is

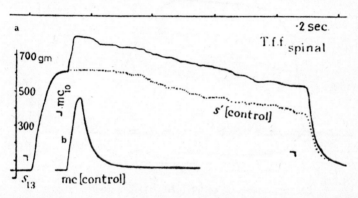

Fig. 9 Experiment illustrating the 'subliminal fringe' in the spinal cat. The muscle *tensor fasciae femoris* delivers the reflex myograms marked 'control' in response to repetitive single stimulation of the two nerves, *internal saphenous* and *musculocutaneous*. The largest reflex in the figure was recorded when both were stimulated together. (Denny-Brown and Sherrington, *J. Physiol.*, 1928, *66*, 175)

adjusted to provide an initial reflex tension of 600 g. gradually dropping to 300 g. during maintained stimulation for some seconds. B, however, is stimulated by a single shock to give a very brief flexion of 500 g. The two are next combined so that B is elicited at the beginning of A running. Then for seconds after cessation of the effect of B, A will continue to be at a considerably higher level of tension than before, dropping gradually from 800 g. to 500 g. With the decerebrate preparation and the crossed extensor such effects are still more striking. A and B may each cause negligible effects of the order of 100 g. separately (Fig. 10) and concurrently elicit a nearly 2,000 g. reflex tension over a much longer time than either alone is capable of maintaining any effect (Eccles and Granit, 1929).

Denny-Brown tells me that when Sherrington first noted such striking effects in their experiments he was a little taken aback. Next morning he appeared at the laboratory with a first sketch of their paper (1928) containing the explanation in terms of the concept of the *subliminal fringe*. This signifies that a central mechanism, clearly dependent upon convergence, has raised the

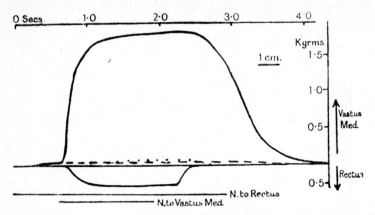

Fig. 10 Decerebrate cat (deafferented). Two muscles, *rectus femoris* and *vastus medialis* (knee extensors) are connected to isometric myographs and their nerves on the crossed side stimulated for the durations marked below the graph. The muscles are made to display contractions on different sides of the baseline. When the single crossed extensor reflexes are elicited as controls, *vastus medialis* responds to both stimuli separately by very small deflexions (dashes and dots), while *rectus femoris* does not respond at all. When both nerves are stimulated together the large reflex deflexions in both muscles (unbroken lines) are obtained. (Eccles and Granit, *J. Physiol.*, 1929, 67, 97)

state of excitability of a large number of fringe neurones in the pool when excited by A, although not enough to make them discharge down their axons. The second stimulus adds enough excitation to the same motoneurones to throw their discharging mechanism into operation. This is so because the *excitatory state* is not an all-or-none affair but is *graded subliminally*. These concepts and the experiments around *subliminal excitation* contain the most important development of the problems of excitation that the isometric myographic technique was responsible for. Subliminal (below-threshold) states of excitation were not new to Sherrington (they were mentioned in *Integrative Action*) but the isometric technique with its emphasis on number of motoneurones chiselled out, questions and answers with greater clarity.

Consider, for instance, the size in gram tension of an individual soleus motor unit. The total maximum for the whole muscle, stimulated to a fused tetanic contraction, is 2,230 g. By staining with osmic acid, the cross-section of the soleus motor nerve, from which the sensory portion is removed by Wallerian degeneration, gives a total of 265 fibres. Eccles and Sherrington (1930) who made such an experiment counted both large and small nerve fibres, but this was a mistake. We know today that the small ones should be subtracted from the total since they do not innervate ordinary (so-called extrafusal) muscle fibres of the kind that give contractions measurable at the tendon. The large ones are 185 in number, taking account of later similar measurements by Hagbarth and Wohlfart. Dividing 2,230 g. by 185 fibres gives the average size in grams of the tetanus tension of a soleus motor unit, which is thus of the order of 12 g.

Returning now, in possession of this figure for the tension in grams of individual soleus motoneurones, to the case when A and B had individually mobilized crossed extensor reflexes of the order of 100 g. (Fig. 10), this value in grams indicates 8 motoneurones. Therefore A and B together ought to mobilize 16 motoneurones (or 200 g.) by an all-or-none mechanism. In the actual experiment they gave a 2,000 g. tension corresponding to 167 of the 185 motoneurones of soleus. The experiment therefore proved that fresh motoneurones had been mobilized from a subliminally excited fringe on which afferents A and B overlapped by converging synapses. No interpretation could make it mean anything else. Isometric myography was good enough for that challenge.

The experiment offered no definite evidence as to the mechanism by which the summated states of excitation could be so prolonged in duration (cf. Figs. 9 and 10). How was the discharge of so many motoneurones so well maintained? Was this a property of the motoneurones themselves or had the stimuli stirred up powerful internuncial mechanisms whose properties differed from those of motoneurones? In the former case a synaptic agent or some property of the cell membrane would have to maintain the excitatory state, in the latter case a relatively brief process in the motoneurone would have to be re-elicited by activity delayed elsewhere. Alexander Forbes (1922), one of Sherrington's disciples, had indeed suggested the existence of delay paths to account for after-discharge, but in Sherrington's judgement after-discharge was 'too prolonged to be . . . explicable by this datum only' (1925). At the time one did not like to imagine that motoneurones differed from inter-neurones, but we shall see later what this problem looks like to-day. Again synaptic thinking pointed the way to precise questions.

Less fortunate in this respect was the conception of *occlusion*, but it is of interest as a reminder of the shortcomings of the isometric analysis of reflex movement. The basic experimental fact behind it is that if, for instance, afferents A and B, maximally stimulated, had elicited reflexes of 1,500 and 1,000 g. respectively, the result of throwing them in simultaneously might be only 1,500 g. or as much as A had given alone. Occlusion as a concept is perfectly clear inasmuch as it states that if A and B overlap by convergence, the full effect of B can be occluded by the full effect of A already having mobilized the very same motoneurones with B-projections (plus others into the bargain). But what does this mean? Is it merely that the muscle fibres were incapable of yielding more tension than they already gave in response to motoneurone discharges set up by the A-afferents alone, or is the limiting factor in the motoneurones (ventral horn cells) themselves? Do both factors contribute? Or is there possibly concealed inhibition which becomes dominant when A and B are thrown in together? It has been argued all along that the essence of synaptic thinking consisted in the lead it gave to unitary anlaysis of nerve cells, for which the concepts of Sherrington proved to be the correct frame of reference because they were directly transferable onto subsequent experiments. Occlusion, alone among them, has not been transferable in this way. Most of the occlusions measured were doubtless caused by saturation at the muscular end of the motor unit. Therefore the concept came to indicate the limit of usefulness of isometric myography rather than any precise central event which, of course, need not mean that one central event could not occlude another in various ways.

Temporal summation, spatial summation and *after-discharge,* mentioned above in different connections, are easily recognized in the examples given in spite of the disguise in which they appear when reflected by isometric myography. These are, in fact, the subjects discussed above, and only after-discharge needs a little additional emphasis. Fig. 11 shows reflexes maintained by after-discharge at so-called *plateau*-level (i.e. at constant tension) in spite of the cessation of afferent stimulation. For the forthcoming discussion of inhibition (below) it is of particular interest to remember that one and the same excitatory effect,

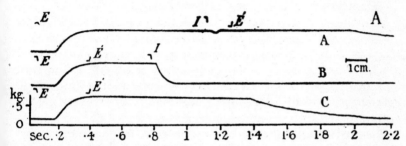

Fig. 11 Crossed extensor reflex in vastocrureus muscle of cat (knee extensor). Inhibition distinguishes between the 'stimulation' plateau of crossed reflexes between *E* and *E'* and the 'after-discharge plateau' after cessation of stimulation. In the reflex response (*A*), inhibition by a single shock *I* only causes a small notch at *I*. When inserted in the after-discharge in record (*B*), *I* causes long-lasting inhibition. The lowermost reflex (*C*) is a repetition of the experiment without *I* to show how well the after-discharge is maintained. (Liddell and Sherrington, *Proc. Roy. Soc.*, 1925, *B97*, 488)

measured in gram tension, may exist with or without the continued support of maintained afferent stimulation. If the *excitatory drive* remains constant despite variations of afferent input, something must have been stored up somewhere during stimulation, and by an extremely potent mechanism at that, since no immediate loss of afferent drive is felt. Alternatively the result means that the motoneurones are capable of maintaining a constant output for a while despite gradual loss of excitatory drive from the afferents. Here again isometric myography served to define a problem worth returning to.

The crossed extensor added the useful notion of *recruitment*[1]

---

[1] Liddell tells me that the word 'recruitment' was evolved after many days of deliberation, the first favourite having been 'increscence'.

to the number of concepts connected with excitation. This implies that under prolonged afferent stimulation reflex tension rises gradually and not in the more explosive *d'emblée* fashion of nociceptive ipsilateral flexion. Isometric myography was accurate enough to support the conclusion that the crossed extensor reflex increased in strength by recruiting fresh neurones from the subliminal fringe (Liddell and Sherrington, 1925). The term recruitment has since been inadequately used by others for any slowly rising state of excitation but its precise meaning should be guarded, respected and preserved. From the beginning this term was couched in the language of unicellular analysis and hence was directly transferable when experimentation with individual motoneurones began. Stimulation of bared afferents is always a compromise, of course, and in this particular case it was rightly held that the recruiting crossed extensor worked itself up to maximum performance under greater rivalry from simultaneously activated inhibitory afferents than did the ipsilateral flexor or, for that matter, the extensor thrust which is also ipsilateral. In this particular case inhibition from the tension receptors in the contracting muscle itself (see below) was responsible for a large proportion of the inhibitory effect. Recruitment versus *d'emblée* myographic opening of reflexes combined with electromyography posed the question of to what extent the increased activity in the electromyogram during reflex activity was due to an increase in the *number* or in the *frequency* of discharges from motoneurones, a problem that in 1929 Adrian and Bronk at Cambridge and Denny-Brown at Oxford solved by actually recording from individual motoneurones (see Chapter 5).

Essentially the concept of recruitment is a development of Sherrington's fundamental principle of reflex action, which maintains that excitability is graded among the individual neurones of a pool. Sherrington himself did not call this fact a principle—a term he reserved for reciprocal innervation—but everything that has happened since in the study of the central nervous system justifies the elevation of the discovery of such subliminal grades of excitation to the high rank of a principle. The subliminal fringe, as defined above, is the recruiting ground for discharge in action. Like the nine-tenths of an iceberg below the surface it is there to determine events. The central nervous system uses it as 'its main functional liaison between co-operative influencers of separate origin. . . . Subliminal fringe at the convergence place forms the "catch-on" for labyrinthine and other reinforcements, and, if we include inhibitory reductions, in their effects of grading and adjusting the local limb and neck reflexes, etc., for posture and for locomotion' (Sherrington, Ferrier Lecture, 1929).

The third reflex responsible for theoretical developments continuing into the present age was the stretch reflex, and in this case integrative aspects became as interesting as problems of synaptic transmission. Sherrington's pioneer contributions originated in the last century. From 1893 onwards he carried out experiments demonstrating the existence of muscular sense organs responding to both stretch and contraction and in *Integrative Action* he refers to earlier work (Brondgeest, 1860) as having demonstrated reflex tone. Vulpian also had said that muscular tone was reflex but Foster was sceptical and so was Schiff, although he knew that ataxia followed dorsal root section. When Sherrington in 1894 published his fundamental paper on the *Anatomical constituents of nerves of skeletal muscles* he had the anatomical evidence, required for progress, in his own demonstration of the sensory nature of the muscle spindle and the tendon organ of Golgi. The best contemporary histological descriptions of muscle spindles were those of Sherrington and the Italian anatomist Ruffini, and the terminology, used to this very day, comes from them. Again the decerebrate animal with its exaggerated extensor tone and stretch reflexes was the preparation that proved particularly useful, and indeed, since tone disappears in anaesthesia, where would he have been without it! (The chronic spinal animal shows tone, but half a month of meticulous animal care is a long preparation time for an experiment.)

It has become customary in recent years to begin the history of the stretch reflex with the classical papers of Liddell and Sherrington (1924–25) based on isometric myography and individual isolated extensor muscles (knee extensors) as if nothing else existed. There is something to be said for this from the didactic point of view: the results are clear and easily understood. Yet the early work had interesting aspects of its own. Sherrington's contributions between 1908 and 1913 dealt mainly with integrative problems; how excitation and inhibition co-operated reciprocally in the acts of standing and stepping. In the nature of things many experiments were carried out with intact limbs in which shortening and lengthening of muscles takes place, and so observations of a different type were made which must not be forgotten in the total account of his achievements. The early work was of particular interest for clinical neurology. In this presentation the story will be unfolded backwards in order to facilitate understanding.

Fig. 12 shows Liddell and Sherrington's result. The limb of the decerebrate preparation is firmly fixed to a stand on a falling table, the quadriceps muscle (knee extensor) is isolated and its free end attached to the isometric torsion wire myograph. T traces the curve of the released falling table. The muscle responds with tension curve M. After the experiment it is paralysed by denervation and now only delivers passive tension P, in response to stretch, and the difference between P and M shows how much of curve M had been active tension caused by the stretch reflex. This reflex would have gone on, diminishing but slowly, had not inhibition been evoked between i and i' which completely knocked out every trace of active tension to leave only the passive effect (P) of stretch on the paralysed muscle.

If in the flexion reflex and the crossed extensor Sherrington had encountered reflexes with wide receptive fields and wide incidence on an assembly of motoneurones belonging to different muscles, then here was a highly *autogenetic* reflex in that it arose in stretch receptors of one particular muscle acting upon itself with some facilitation of synergists. When stretch was rapid, an initial phasic response could be clearly distinguished from a reflex contraction maintained at a lower level of tension. This was particularly prominent in good decerebrate preparations, but absent in spinal ones in which something of the phasic component might still remain.

This, then, was for Sherrington the basic reflex in standing, the one counteracting gravity (stretching extensors) and preventing the animal from falling. It provided the clue to an analysis of decerebrate rigidity, 'exaggerated standing' as Sherrington had called it, and with it, by and by, many pieces of a large puzzle began to fall into their right places—some of them in Sherrington's own time. He, of course, realized the difficulty in speaking of exaggerated standing as a reflex response to stretch when the decerebrate animal was stiff even when lying down on its side, without gravitational pull on the extensors. This was explained by the concept of *release*, introduced into neurology by that great eccentric thinker Hughlings Jackson, but actually well known from early cerebellar physi-

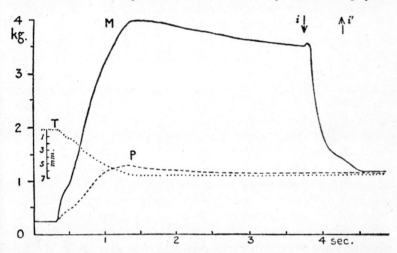

Fig. 12 Decerebrate cat. Whole quadriceps muscle is connected to the falling table which stretches it along curve *T*, with inset ordinates in millimetres. The muscle responds with stretch reflex *M*, which is inhibited by ipsilateral mixed nerve (*n. peroneus* and *popliteus* together) between *i* and *i'*. After completion of the experiment on stretch reflex, the nerve is cut to demonstrate that, without the added reflex contraction, stretch only causes the myographic response *P*. Note that inhibition removes reflex completely, so that the myograph level after inhibition actually coincides with *P*. (Liddell and Sherrington, *Proc. Roy. Soc.*, 1924, *B96*, 212)

ology. In Magendie's laboratory Foderà (1823) had seen the rigidity ensuing upon cerebellar ablations in birds and mammals and had ascribed it to a release from a restraint exercised by the cerebellum. Sherrington now had to assume that in decerebrate rigidity the motoneurones were released from some inhibitory tonic influence residing above the level of the section in the brain stem. Why then did the rigidity disappear when the afferent roots were cut, as Sherrington himself had already shown in his first paper? He never ceased to emphasize that decerebrate rigidity required intact afferent supply. The unsolved question of why the decerebrate preparation responded with greatly exaggerated stretch reflexes in the absence of muscle stretch, as when lying on its side, will for the moment be left with Sherrington's statement (1932) that decerebrate rigidity is not a pure, uncomplicated Jacksonian release of standing. A new set of ideas and recording from single units were required for further advance (see Chapter 7).

Going back now to Sherrington's early work on tone or 'reflex posture', as he preferred to call it even when he did not hesitate to speak about the tonic and phasic components of the stretch reflex (1906, 1925), one of the most important disclosures was the demonstration of inhibitory endings in the rigid muscles of the decerebrate preparation. When the limb was forcibly bent, tension first rose in the extensors under the pull exercised on them and this is the stretch reflex illustrated in Fig. 12. On further pull from continued bending of the limb, the tension suddenly gave way in a 'clasp-knife' fashion owing to stimulation of inhibitory tension receptors capable, in the end, of overcoming the effects from the excitatory organs responsible for the stretch reflex. The limb stayed in the new position and very slowly returned to the original state of rigid extension. For this reason the inhibitory response was called the 'lengthening reaction', the term implying that the limb had to remain for a while in the new position and not merely reveal the clasp-knife interruption of active tensile stress. As a corollary to this mode of behaviour, the stiff extensors of the intact limb remained shortened for a while if the leg was forcibly extended, so as to make the two ends of the extensor muscles approach each other, Sherrington's 'shortening reaction'. These two reactions, Sherrington said (1913) 'imbue the tonus of the muscle with plasticity'. It is clear from his comparisons with smooth muscle (1908) that by 'plasticity' he meant the property of the extensors to maintain practically the same tone (tension) in spite of great variations of length. Since the muscle-machine under constant efferent stimulation produces active tension proportional to its length over a considerable range, some automatic adjustment of reflex output must take place if the muscle is to preserve its tension independently of length.

Out of this complex totality, let us first take the inhibitory tension-sensitive endings in the muscles as something tangible and easy to understand, recalling that really high tensions in muscles are set up in contraction and not in stretch. Sherrington's work on 'autogenetic inhibition', as he called it, was done at a time when he used isotonic myography and so had fairly small variations of tension even when stretching forcibly in the manner just described or, alternatively, by stimulating the severed distal portion of the motor nerve to the flexor in order to stretch the extensor (1908) by the contraction of its antagonist. Sherrington could not explain the two 'plastic' modes of reaction, but he emphasized that they depended on intact afferent nerves from the extensor muscles concerned, that they disappeared in certain extreme forms of rigidity and under strychnine, when autogenetic inhibition also failed to occur, and he pointed out that they were reminiscent of cataleptic states in man. The autogenetic extensor inhibition was found to elicit a reciprocal excitation in the corresponding extensor of the opposite limb. This was identified as Philippson's reflex (1905).

The questions Sherrington now ran up against required some knowledge of the properties of the muscle receptors. Discussing *Problems of Muscular Receptivity* in his Linacre Lecture in 1924 he pointed out that there would be separate recorders of muscle-length and of muscle-tension and suggested that the latter function was subserved by the Golgi tendon organs. The muscle spindles, he thought, were stimulated by active muscular contraction because they had motor nerves, as Cipollone (1898) had shown by Wallerian degeneration. In that same year Forbes and his collaborators also published a paper demonstrating afferent mass impulses on contraction of muscles. In a letter to Forbes from Rouen (September 13, 1924) Sherrington wrote: 'Your demonstration of action currents in the afferent nerve resulting from active contraction of the muscle supplies a long-felt want. Until that demonstration was forthcoming there remained open the possibility that proprioceptors, although replying to passively imposed lengthenings (and shortenings) and tensions in muscle and tendon might conceivably be so contrived as to be shielded from stimulation by *active* contraction' (Fulton's collection of letters). Fulton worked out the latter line of thought with Pi-Suñer (1927–28) when they distinguished between stretch receptors in series and in parallel with the muscle fibres. The former would register tension in both stretch and contraction, the latter would be unloaded in contraction and hence cease to deliver information. They pointed out that tendon organs are connected 'in series', muscle spindles 'in parallel'. Sherrington, however, was worried about the motor fibres to the muscle spindles' own so-called intrafusal muscles. What was their rôle? No further advance in understanding was possible without actually recording from afferent fibres belonging to the two fundamental types of end-organs (see Chapter 5). Sherrington ended his Linacre Lecture thus:

Muscular receptivity offers a wide field, and our view of it has perforce been but a glimpse. That glimpse, however, may have served to show that through their own nervous arcs the muscles have a voice in their own management and co-ordination, and that they are, moreover, not motor machines only but sense organs as well. Only by fuller study of them in these aspects can we know how best to use them.

The stretch reflex has contributed a major share to the theoretical study of inhibition but, as so much of the modern interpretation comes from understanding not reached until after Sherrington's time, this work is better taken up in Chapter 7. Nevertheless it is clear that the monosynaptic nature of this reflex, its high afferent conduction velocity also implying a low threshold to electrical stimuli, and the ease with which different natural stimuli (tendon taps, slow extension, contraction) could be used for comparisons with artificial ones, made it the natural choice for those looking for tools useful in the study of synaptic problems, as different from the integrative type of physiology chiefly pursued by Sherrington but pursued in a manner that focused light on the synaptic events. Sherrington's own theoretical formulations concerning the latter came to depend very much on experimental tests carried out with the ipsilateral flexor and the crossed extensor. From them, mainly, he worked out the concepts of the central excitatory state (c.e.s.) and the central inhibitory state (c.i.s.). We have already met the graded, long-lasting rise of excitability that was seen after a conditioning afferent stimulus and which served as the basis for summation of excitation as tested by a second stimulus. This is the central excitatory state, and a corner-stone in Sherrington's teaching was that there is an equivalent inhibitory state of opposite sign so that excitation and inhibition would add up algebraically, both being active states capable of gradation. Based on work with Eccles on the flexor reflex, the schematic curve of Fig. 13 was plotted. One conditioning shock sets up an excitatory state, tested by its facilitating influence on the

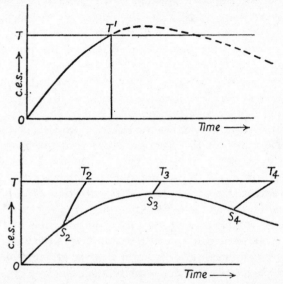

Fig. 13 Diagrammatic representation of the rise and fall of the central excitatory state of the flexor reflex in response to a single afferent shock. *T* in both diagrams is the level needed for a threshold response and in the upper diagram a single shock is strong enough to make the central excitatory state reach firing level, *T*. In the lower diagram, a first shock gives sub-threshold response and further subliminal shocks, applied alternately at S_2, S_3, and S_4, make the excitatory state reach threshold as shown. (Eccles and Sherrington, *Proc. Roy. Soc.*, 1931, *B107*, 511)

responses to stimulation by a second shock. This effect is seen to last some time.

The most important early experiments on pitting graded inhibition against graded excitation are found in his Thirteenth Note on reciprocal innervation, *On the Antagonism between Reflex Inhibition and Reflex Excitation*, from which he concluded, 'the reflex effect of concurrent stimulation of excitatory afferent nerve with inhibitory afferent nerve on the vasto-crureus preparation is an algebraic summation of the effects obtainable from the two nerves singly, as v. Cyon has maintained for the heart' (*vagus* versus *accelerans* stimulation). The inhibitory-excitatory interplay presupposes interaction at a common site. 'As to the common locus of operation, the point of collision of the antagonistic influences, it seems permissible to suppose either that it lies at a synapse, in which case the opposed influences may be thought of as altering oppositely the permeability of the synaptic membrane, or that it lies in the substance of the 'central' portion of a neurone, probably of the motoneurone itself . . .' (1908).

Sherrington was always reluctant to commit himself to definite views on the actual mechanisms of excitation and inhibition, whether 'neutralization' of one by the other (a term he used in 1925) was chemical or electrical, though he took note of advance elsewhere and freely discussed possible alternatives. His own final views are best expressed in the Nobel Lecture (1932) where he said: 'It is commonly held that nerve-excitation consists essentially in the local depolarization of a polarized membrane on the surface of the neurone. As to "central excitation", it is difficult to suppose such depolarization of the cell-surface can be graded any more than can that of the fibre. But its antecedent step (facilitation) might be graded, e.g. subliminal. Local depolarizations having occurred the difference of potential thus arisen gives a current which disrupts the adjacent polarization membrane, and so the "excitation" travels. As to inhibition the suggestion is made that it consists in the temporary stabilization of the surface-membrane which excitation would break down. As tested against a standard excitation the inhibitory stabilization is found to present various degrees of stability. The inhibitory stabilization of the membrane might be pictured as a heightening of the "resting" polarization, somewhat on the lines of an electrotonus. Unlike the excitation-depolarization it would not travel; and, in fact the inhibitory state does not travel.' (The reference to excitation travelling and inhibition being stationary simply means that excitatory depolarization of the neurone at the threshold generates an impulse or action potential which travels outwards into its axon, while inhibition consists in the prevention by an opposite process of the depolarization increasing until it generates an impulse.)

By the time this was written (1932), Adrian, who shared the Nobel prize with Sherrington, had analysed the nature of the sensory message in terms of single end-organs and single fibres (Adrian and Zotterman, 1926) and so one knew that the central cells were bombarded by fast impulses whose frequency reflected stimulus intensity. Therefore it seemed natural to imagine the excitatory state being built up by a barrage of such impulses, some inhibitory, some excitatory, interacting at the surface to produce the net depolarization that the relative number of explosive events of opposite sign would permit. As such, impulses producing effects of opposite sign were essentially alike, and the opposite effects could be localized to the terminals or to the neuronal side of the synaptic cleft according to what one thought sensible. On this point there was no evidence, but Sherrington in his theoretical study of 1925 favoured the idea that essentially similar terminals 'may yet act in the perikaryon on subsurface material of different kind so that one may cause there an excitatory, the other the inhibitory response' (p. 533).

Sherrington's views on inhibition thus came to a final conceptual focus around events not specified in every detail but centred around the motoneurone membrane. They left room for chemical (1925) or electrical mechanisms (1932). The former was actualized by Loewi's discovery in the mid-twenties that stimulation of the vagus or the accelerans inhibited or accelerated the heart by means of two chemical intermediaries, the *Vagusstoff* and the *Acceleransstoff*, which proved to be closely imitable by acetylcholine and adrenalin respectively. Sherrington's leading idea was 'neutralization' or, as he also expressed it, 'algebraical summation', and it rested on the postulate that the two antagonistic processes were genuine events at two different kinds of synapse striking a balance point at the motoneurone. This does not mean that he was unaware of complex interactions in interneurones. Scientific thinking must necessarily advance by clarifying one thing at a time, while tentacles are sent out feeling for fresh openings elsewhere, and Sherrington's thinking was conditioned by his experimental concentration on the 'final common path' with myography as the leading technique. Naturally, since this ended in muscle, the replies to his questions emerged in terms of additions or subtractions of gram tension or mm. contraction. Since excitation from work on peripheral nerve had come to mean membrane depolarization, it also seemed natural to think of inhibition as some kind of opposite repolarizing process stabilizing the membrane.

Sherrington's intuition proved sound (see later) and synaptic thinking triumphant when motoneurones came to be studied individually by various techniques. How good was his evidence when he so definitely located inhibition to specific synapses? Could he ever defend himself experimentally against a totally different line of argument, originating with Keith Lucas (1917), and making inhibition consequent upon previous excitation? Lucas' main idea was that, since, with the peripheral nerve-muscle preparation, excitation left a brief period of refractoriness and fast repetitive stimulation blocked the muscle contraction, the so-called Wedensky inhibition, why invent something else for central inhibition?

The main reason was because Sherrington had originally (1906) started out from the perfectly genuine inhibitions of the vagus nerve on the heart and that of the *Astacus* claw (see p. 56) which provided analogies just as good as those pointed out by Lucas. In conversation Sherrington once emphasized that when he took up experimentation, Ewald Hering's ideas about two fundamental opposite processes, anabolism and katabolism, played a great rôle at Cambridge. One was therefore on the look-out for opposite processes in cellular activity. In *Integrative Action* he had mentioned this: 'Hering, Gaskell, Verworn, and others have taught us to attach important external functions to the assimilatory (anabolic) phase. The first mentioned has dealt with the visual sensations in assimilation-dissimilation pairs. Black-white sensation is thus traced to a pair of reactions affecting the trophism of the cell in exactly opposite directions. Gaskell relates vagus inhibition of the heart to the throwing of the cardiac muscle-cell into a phase predominantly anabolic. . . .' *Integrative Action* contains terms borrowed from Hering's work (spinal induction) and comparisons between reflex and visual events are quite common. Sherrington had also met Hering and greatly respected him. Henry Head had worked for two years (1884–86) in Hering's laboratory in Prague. Historically Sherrington's attitude to these problems was a legitimate descendant of a great tradition in physiology into which he infused his own synaptic thinking, and it was really Lucas who was the revolutionary, in spite of the conservative type of theorizing that he advocated.

After this digression let us return to answer the question raised: how convincing was Sherrington's evidence in favour of an active inhibitory process which could occur independently and not necessarily as a sequence to excitation? The arguments all centred around observations demonstrating identical properties of excitation and inhibition, disregarding sign. Thus there was inhibitory recruitment, a long inhibitory after-discharge, summation of subliminal inhibitory effects. Long after-effects following brief inhibitory volleys were studied by Liddell and Sherrington in their paper on *Recruitment and some other Features of Reflex Inhibition* (1925), later by Eccles and Sherrington (1931). If inhibition really had been dependent upon preceding excitation, how was it possible that, when pitted against excitation, it never was enhanced by it? Why did it oppose *succeeding* excitation? Actually, 'neutralization' always occurred. The results on inhibition were briefly summarized by Sherrington in 1932: 'Inhibition like excitation can be induced in a "resting" centre. The only test we have for the inhibition is excitation. Existence of an excited state is not a prerequisite for the production of inhibition; inhibition can exist apart from excitation no less than, when called forth against an excitation already in progress, it can suppress or moderate it. The centripetal volley which excites a "centre" finds, if preceded by an inhibitory volley, the centre so treated is already irresponsive or partly so.'

Whatever other mechanisms could be forced to explain central excitation and inhibition, as the balance of evidence stood when Sherrington, after forty years of experimentation, laid down his tools, it must be concluded that he had definitely established *synaptic* excitation and *synaptic* inhibition as the mirror images of two genuine and opposite processes. These had been endowed with properties which in a decisive manner guided experimentation in this field in the future.

Chapter 4

The Prolific Years

In the life of every scientist who contributes something of importance to his field there must have been a long period of intense devotion to experimentation, reading, study, and thinking, taxing the patience of a dear wife who would find it difficult to understand the sudden shifts in the husband's moods from distant solitude and absent-mindedness to moments of obvious elation depending upon intellectual revelations difficult to share with others. In Sherrington's life 1895 to 1913, the years at Liverpool, were such a period of intense creation and study. So far only those aspects of his work at Liverpool have been presented that became normative for the future development of theoretical neurophysiology as we know it today, but his accomplishments included many other things which alone would have made a lesser man satisfied with his day of labour.

During those years Sherrington wrote *Integrative Action*, he was responsible for some of the best chapters in Schäfer's *Textbook of Physiology*, those on the spinal cord, the brain stem, cerebellum and medulla oblongata, on cutaneous sensations, and on the muscular sense, all of which are still highly readable, forward-looking products of well-digested experimental experience and vast reading; he taught, even physiological chemistry, sat on committees, and published reports as professors had to do then as now; he built and organized a new laboratory, and wrote much of the poetry in the *Assaying of Brabantius* not to mention the experimental papers, from which only some leading ideas can be extracted here. He wrote too much, said Cushing, but life was exciting and the cup was full.

What would Sherrington have retorted, had he known of Cushing's remark? Possibly what he said to me once when we were talking about John Fulton's biography of Harvey Cushing: 'You know, the life of a great surgeon is not really exciting, except, of course, from the patient's point of view.' We discussed the subject at some length and Sherrington began to recall names of surgeons whom he would regard as exceptions. The two he mentioned were Lord Lister and Wilder Penfield, both also scientists and physiologists.

In those days professors did not have secretaries but Sherrington's wife took upon herself the secretarial duties needed in the laboratory and also for his international work, because at the time and for fifteen years Sherrington was Anglo-American secretary of the International Congresses of Physiology. Sherrington and Ethel Wright of Preston, Suffolk, had been married in 1891 when he was made Professor Superintendent of the Brown Institution.

There was not much of a laboratory when Sherrington arrived in Liverpool. He described it to me as 'almost a shed'. But the University found a benefactor in the Rev. S. A. Thompson Yates and in October 1898 the new laboratories for physiology and pathology, bearing Thompson's name and built by Messrs. A. Waterhouse & Son, were opened with a solemn act. Several eminent guests were present, among them Lord Lister and the pathologist, Professor Virchow, in whose laboratory in Berlin Sherrington had worked when he returned from Puglia. The donor gave an opening Address published in the *Thompson-Yates Laboratories Report*, volume I, edited by the two professors (later, Sir) Rubert Boyce (1863–1911) and Sherrington. In that volume of 238 pages octavo a large number of papers came from Sherrington's laboratory.

The architect, Sherrington told me, laughing heartily, discussed with the two professors what kind of an emblem should be placed on the wall of the new building. In the end they decided in favour of an idea symbolizing Pathologia and Physiologia by two attractive female figures in the manner shown in Plate 7 and decided to have them executed by a sculptor in the likeness of Mrs Boyce and Mrs Sherrington. This may have been a well-kept secret, as I began to suspect when I asked Professor R. A. Morton of Liverpool University to obtain a reproduction for this book and also mentioned the story to the present physiologist at Liverpool, Professor R. A. Gregory; neither of them knew it.

7

As a consequence the grime and soot of sixty-four years have now been removed from the relief and the young charming wives, attired à la Grecque, can be admired in their original beauty, possibly somewhat idealized.

In the opening address by the Rev. Thompson Yates there were some words which Sherrington at least would have listened to with appreciation: '. . . I would urge you all, whatever your profession, not to be satisfied with knowledge merely professional. You will make better doctors, better men of Science, better citizens, and be of greater use to your fellow-creatures if you know something of the side of human thought expressed in the words Philosophy, Poetry, History, Literature. You have not time? Then make it somehow; I believe we all can do so, and make ourselves better men and women by the self-denial involved in the manufacture.'

The *University of Liverpool Recorder* published in January 1960 an extract from the *Memories of Sherrington* by his son, C. E. R. Sherrington, which referred to the Liverpool years.

Writing to his mother in October, 1895, from Grove Park, Liverpool, he described the house as in many ways like his devoted home at Edgehill, Ipswich. . . . [In the city he found] the distances small, and the traffic countrified, and the shops too.

He was pleased with the climate which was bright and sunny compared with that of London; and he was well received both by his colleagues and the great Merseyside families who ruled in the shipping world and society and, on occasion, also proved willing to support his experiments.

One of Sherrington's early students, an otologist and surgeon, H. V. Forster, in a brief address to the laboratory at Liverpool (1961) has some interesting reminiscences of the young professor, worth putting on record:

I can see him now, coming through that door on my left in his black gown (1907). There was nothing of the showman about him, but much humility and respect. . . . We had heard with much curiosity that at Liverpool when working with Grünbaum, Sherrington had mapped out areas of function in the motor cortex of the chimpanzee and even the gorilla, and in due time after instruction about the reciprocal action of antagonistic muscles we were introduced to its reversal in the leg area here . . . both in strychnine and tetanus toxaemia. . . . It is not surprising that we were especially attentive to his ideas on the predominance of the brain and the head as physiologically conceived.

Forster had some old lecture notes on this:
'The segments lying at the leading pole of the animal, armed as they are with the great "distance" sense organs, constitute what is termed the "head". [Then he goes on to enquire whether this dominance of the leading segments which is traceable in the receptors of the exteroceptive field applies in the field of reception which is termed the proprioceptive.] The labyrinth (for example) is the chief proprioceptor of the leading segment of the body which is the head. The labyrinth keeps the world right side up for the organism by keeping the organism right side up to the external world.'

Sherrington's ideas on the rôle of proprioceptors, the labyrinth and the cerebellum in muscular tone had already acquired their general form. Sherrington spoke of the cerebellum (in Dr Forster's notes) as the head ganglion of the proprioceptive system, as he was wont to do to the end. The cerebrum was the ganglion of the distance receptors. He liked to venerate its conception as the 'neo pallium', the pallium being 'that woollen covering, an emblem of archiepiscopal dignity' built up chiefly on impressions from the eyes with their capacity for binocular vision. His master's voice is also vividly there in the notes on the knock-out in the Prize Ring which excited the young student: 'The knock-out blow where the lower jaw conveys concussion to the otocyst, reduces in a moment a vigorous athlete to an unstrung bulk of flesh whose weight alone determines its attitude, if indeed a reactionless mass can be described as possessing attitude at all.'

A. S. F. Grünbaum (1869–1921) whom Forster mentioned is better known under the name of Leyton (after 1915, by deed poll). He was Sherrington's assistant at Liverpool and later became Professor of Pathology at Leeds. Like Sherrington he was a Gonville and Caius man who had also been at St Thomas's Hospital. In 1896 Leyton had worked in Vienna where he devised the agglutination test in typhoid fever but felt that he had too few cases and so could not publish it. Widal then, on two cases, preceded him by a few weeks (Sherrington). Leyton and Sherrington carried out work, still quoted today, on the motor cortex of the chimpanzee, orang-utan, and gorilla. Other members of the group were T. Graham Brown, F. W. Mott, and E. Schuster. In 1901 Cushing joined them for a month. A young American, R. S. Woodworth, proved good and was tempted to stay on after having studied with Sherrington a 'pseudo-affective reflex' in the decerebrate preparation, recently taken up again by R. K. S. Lim, but finally he returned to the States to become Professor of Psychology at Columbia University and live to a great age as the revered Nestor of the American psychologists. In a letter to me (January 27, 1954) containing some reminiscences from Liverpool, Woodworth among other things pointed out that Sherrington began his day with research, and not, as most professors, with minor matters of administration and instruction. Prominent among foreign guest workers at Liverpool were Rudolf Magnus (see below), H. E. Hering, discoverer of the carotid baro-receptor reflexes, and the Austrian, Alfred Fröhlich, well known for his description of the so-called adiposo-genital syndrome. In his Sherrington Lecture of 1952 Fulton has some extracts from Cushing's diary and concludes: 'Gay and busy days these were, and Sir Charles and Alfred Fröhlich still recall them with a lively sense of pleasure, as did Harvey Cushing while he lived.'

'Glancing back in perspective,' says C. E. R. Sherrington in the *Liverpool Recorder*, 'the years at Liverpool were, I believe, the happiest in his life, and my mother's too,' and small wonder. Peace prevailed in the world and work in the new laboratory was exciting. Guest workers came and stayed on to experiment under Sherrington's guidance; visitors from the United States and Canada in those days took the route by Liverpool, and international contacts with the European continent were developed, officially, by his work as Anglo-American secretary of the congresses, unofficially as well, by travel for pleasure during holidays. The young couple loved Paris. His wife, being partly of French origin, spoke the language fluently but may not have shared her husband's taste for browsing among the *bouquiniste* stalls on the Rive Gauche and hunting up incunabula and old books in libraries to lay the groundwork for his study of Jean Fernel and the ancient history of the Latin Quarter. For this suspicion of mine Fulton is responsible because he mentions the following incident.

Sherrington in 1935 'summoned me to his room and with a slightly apologetic expression showed me some forty medical incunabula stored away in the back of a large drawer. With a smile and twinkle that all book collectors understand [Fulton, of course, was a passionate collector of old books], he said: "Dear Ethel, my devoted wife, doesn't fully share my interests in incunabula and I am passing them on to the British Museum."'

With some right, Wilder Penfield speaks of the 'celebrated' contributions by Leyton and Sherrington to our knowledge of the functional organization of the motor cortex in primates. He should know, having himself explored the motor areas in man more extensively than anybody else. The question naturally arises as to what Sherrington could add to the findings of Fritsch and Hitzig (1870) in Germany and of Ferrier (1873–81) in England. They were the pioneers. Sir Victor Horsley (around 1890) followed up Ferrier's work. The Liverpool group started in the early nineties but publication followed some twelve years after Beevor and Horsley. The full report came in 1917, after Horsley's death, possibly because Sherrington wanted to avoid a second polemic with the latter. In a letter (in Fulton's collection) from Sherrington to Dr Mond, who took care of the expense of buying monkeys, Sherrington pointed out that he could not confirm Horsley. Between Goltz on the one hand and Fritsch, Hitzig, and Ferrier on the other, surgery had improved a great deal. Animal care and surgery underwent further improvement with Leyton and Sherrington, the latter, as all his pupils know, being extremely careful in his surgical work. Of Leyton, Sherrington said: 'He combined in rare measure enthusiasm for research with a critical, and, indeed, highly self-critical attitude of mind.'

In those days difficulties were considerable. Ferrier, probably the most skilful of the early workers, had, for instance, misplaced the visual centres and as late as 1905 Horsley, in a well-known and important paper with Clarke, had found that electrical stimulation of the surface of the cerebellum did not produce any response in the animal. Yet it is well known that both movement and inhibition of movement can be elicited from the cerebellar cortex, as shown by Sherrington in 1896.

The extremely detailed map of localization in the motor cortex of primates which Sherrington and Leyton published became the accepted standard for many years, but equally important were the concepts they reached. They emphasized the functional instability and deviation of the response that became evident as soon as the explored point was sufficiently small and tested often enough over some time. A cortical point representing, say, extension of the index finger is connected to a number of other points (cells) which represent various combinations in which this movement is elicited. A contraction of a particular facial muscle may take part in chewing, in mimetic acts, in the production of sound. 'And in the motor cortex this discrete "representation" of small local items of movement, each highly co-ordinated with others yet separably elicitable, instead of becoming less evident with ascent to the higher types of hemisphere, becomes more so. Thus, it is more evident in cat and dog than in rabbit, more evident in the Macaque than in cat or dog, in baboon than in Macaque, in gibbon than in baboon, and in the chimpanzee, orang, and gorilla than in gibbon. . . . Phenomena such as "reversal of response" (from one type of movement to its opposite), "facilitation", and "deviation of response" prominent in cortical responses and accounting for the functional instability of cortical motor points, are indicative of the enormous wealth of mutual associations existing between the separable motor cortical points. Those associations must also be a characteristic part of the machinery by which the synthetic powers of that cortex are made possible.'

We have not since found it necessary to alter in any fundamental way the picture Leyton and Sherrington gave of the functional organization of the motor cortex even though the number of sites in the cortex from which motor effects can be elicited has since increased.

Localization of function has always been a field in which physiologists, anatomists, neurologists, and neurosurgeons take a common interest. It is hardly necessary to dwell upon the need for functional maps in clinical work. One example may suffice. Hughlings Jackson, from studies of focal epileptogenic fits, had predicted the localization of the motor area one year before Fritsch and Hitzig discovered it by direct electrical stimulation.

Sherrington followed this work through with great interest, and when Penfield discovered places in the brain of man which on stimulation during operations made the patients recall long-lost incidents in their lives, his old teacher looked at him with a quizzical smile and said: 'It must be nice to hear the preparation speak to you.'

To this time at Liverpool belongs a story that has often been told but which is so characteristic of him that I must re-tell it, in spite of my intention to include very little of the well-known anecdotal flora of Sherringtoniana. The professor was reported in *The Daily Mail* as having said in a lecture: 'One day after a visit I turned back, pondering what the chimpanzees might do when I left them. I stooped down and looked through the keyhole, and there the chimpans' eye—I mean the chimpanzee's eye—met mine. The same thought had struck us both, but the chimpanzee, being a lady, had got there first.'

With some justification one might say that much of the work that Sherrington did on the supraspinal structures was of the kind that in itself would not have given him the unique position he now occupies in the history of neurophysiology and neurology. It was important enough in its day to place him in the front rank among those who influenced progress in these fields, and probably it was more reliable than that of many of his best-known contemporaries. Why then did he spend so much time experimenting on the brain when the rich harvest lay in the spinal cord with the conceptual advance that the better-known organization of that structure made possible, as explained above?

The answer has already been indicated in the extracts from Dr Forster's lecture notes. The spinal cord is a servant of that great master, the brain. It may be an exaggerated metaphor to compare the cord with a grand piano requiring its 'supraspinal' virtuoso, but the simile is useful in order to explain why Sherrington and most of his successors sooner or later have been irresistibly drawn towards the higher centres, mostly, I suppose, coming to the conclusion that in the end the relative precision of work in the lower portion of the neuraxis provides greater satisfaction. On the other hand, experience with the organ of supreme control is required by any one interested in reflexology and the spinal cord. Without it, the integrative action of the central nervous system can never be fully apprehended.

Thus with Sherrington, who on Gaskell's advice had fled from the *clair-obscure* of cortical physiology into the relative daylight that study of the spinal cord seemed to promise, was forced back to his original point of departure by observations and circumstances which should now be briefly reviewed in order to illuminate his development as an experimenter and thinker.

During his visits to Goltz's laboratory, Sherrington had become acquainted with the general symptoms exhibited by the spinal dog and so was familiar with the fact that removal of supraspinal control led to a state of shock characterized by great depression of response to stimulation in the musculature below the section. This was a striking demonstration of the importance of the higher centres. In many respects this condition was known to develop in different ways in dog and in man where it was familiar, as a result of accidents for instance. Sherrington had recourse to monkeys and soon found that both permanent damage and initial shock are disproportionately greater in monkeys than in cat and dog, and following out his case he separated 'shock' as such from the later effects of isolation-dystrophy. He found monkey and man more similar in their symptoms than man and dog. 'The symptoms of shock, in many monkeys, persist for days instead of hours and minutes, as in cat and dog' (Marshall Hall Prize Address 'On the spinal animal', 1899). This is in keeping with the law of increasing encephaliz-ation of control upwards along the phylogenetic scale (von Monakow).

Sherrington studied the spinal state with his customary atten-tion to every detail of behaviour, sensory, motor, vegetative, and his work became normative both for the clinic and the laboratory. Several of his pupils have continued this work (Denny-Brown, Fulton, Liddell, McCouch, Rioch), and for thirty years the spinal or the spinalized, decerebrate animal has been a favourite preparation in which to study the spinal cord deprived of central control, especially in work on problems of synaptic transmission. For such problems it is often necessary to simplify the neural circuit. Thus, for instance, Lloyd in his analysis of monosynaptic transmission in the forties found this preparation a valuable tool.

In a similar way other supraspinal structures were drawn into Sherrington's sphere of interest. In 1896–98 he made the fundamental observation that decerebrate rigidity could be inhibited by stimulating the anterior portion of the cerebellum, unilaterally, if only one side of it was stimulated. This work was developed by one of his later pupils, Frédéric Bremer (1922), professor at Brussels, one of the best-known neurologists and neurophysiologists of the present day. Sherrington reported his finding in 1906 and published it in 1907. One month later the same result was reported by Loewenthal and Horsley. Sherrington went on to describe in considerable detail a number of other sites from which decerebrate rigidity could be inhibited.

In many other ways the problem of supraspinal control engaged Sherrington's attention, in connection with tone, standing, and postural reflexes in general. The matter seemed to him very important, and rightly so, because nearly all movements have a postural component. The importance of posture is sometimes emphasized by saying that it is the starting-point and end-point of every movement. But posture, as Ramsay Hunt remarked, accompanies 'movement like a shadow'. Stanley Cobb (another Sherrington disciple) writes that 'they coalesce and often cannot be separated'. As an example, Sherrington said, 'one might take the scratch reflex elicited by an "artificial flea" in the form of a faint faradic current tickling the skin behind the ear. The dog executes a most complex series of postural reflexes to balance itself while scratching. An array of muscles is co-ordinated or integrated in this act'.

If one were to describe the many fundamental observations Sherrington made on posture, they would fill this book. Alongside his experimental and conceptual advance towards the definition of properties of synaptic action at membranes of single neurones, his work on tone, or posture as he preferred to call it, stands as a monument *aere perennius* in a triad whose third component is the analysis of reciprocal innervation. I place them in this order but we have seen that Sherrington himself put reciprocal innervation first, probably because to him it must have been the great eye-opener for the general problem of inhibition. And so this particular conquest of his youth became surrounded by an aura of delight that never vanished

What we now call the Sherringtonian type of decerebrate

rigidity, discussed above, is a kind of extensor spasm or exaggerated tone dependent upon intact afferents from the rigid muscles. But it is not the only form of extensor rigidity, as Sherrington very well understood. Ablation of the cerebellum will also cause rigidity, and comparing this state with the one ensuing upon intercollicular section Sherrington with penetrating insight concluded: 'That the two conditions are identical I am not convinced' (1898). Later, but in his lifetime, Pollock and Davis contributed experiments which made it clear that cerebellar rigidities did not vanish upon de-afferentation. Sherrington himself showed that rigidity in the forelimbs increased when the spinal cord was sectioned at some lower level. This finding is known as the Schiff-Sherrington phenomenon because Schiff had made a similar observation on the frog (1859). In 1936 it was taken up again by T. C. Ruch. Today we know a great deal more about the various factors determining muscular tone (see later) and they have been well analysed by Moruzzi in his important monograph with Dow, the latter responsible for the clinical part (*Physiology and pathology of the cerebellum*, 1958).

The restricted space available for discussion of each subject should not lead to the rash conclusion that nothing was known about supraspinal factors influencing tone before Sherrington arrived on the stage. He had had great predecessors, especially in the field of cerebellar physiology, and at least two names must be mentioned, those of Flourens (1794–1867), in perspective one of the greatest of all French physiologists, and Luciani (1842–1919), practically a contemporary, who had published his famous book, *Il Cervelletto*, in 1891. Ewald, whom Sherrington knew well, had pointed out that destruction of the vestibular organs reduces the tone of the skeletal musculature on the side of the operation. Sherrington's standpoint that the cerebellum might be regarded as the central station for the control of proprioceptive reflexes therefore had much support in both old and contemporary experimentation.

Is this notion still valid? There are those who deny this, basing themselves upon what Moruzzi has called the 'unexpected discovery' that the cerebellum receives important projections from exteroceptive senses such as the eye, the ear, and, in particular, the skin. This was found almost simultaneously in independent electrophysiological experiments by Adrian, and also by Dow and by Snider (1942–43) and co-workers. But why need such findings exclude the cerebellum from its rôle as 'proprioceptive head ganglion'? It seems reasonable that an organ for proprioceptive control would need all that information from exteroceptive senses. Posture, after all, is part of every movement and movement takes place in surroundings continuously measured by our exteroceptive senses aided by the vestibular organs of balance and the endings in muscles and joints. The cerebellum, we might say today, in expanding Sherrington's concept, computes sensory information for the purpose of postural control. Space does not permit us to discuss other tasks allotted to this organ (cf. the Dow and Moruzzi monograph, mentioned above).

Sherrington's work on muscular tone had led him to the final conclusion that, in mammals, tone was due to postural reflexes, just as Brondgeest at Utrecht (1860) had found it to be the case in frogs and rabbits. Brondgeest's work had immediately been repeated and confirmed by Dr Rosenthal in the laboratory of Du Bois-Reymond, who added a note to this effect in his *Archives* where the Dutch worker had published his findings. These problems occupied Sherrington very much at the time (in 1908) when Magnus arrived in Liverpool and possibly the latter had been impressed by the 'reflex figures' which the decerebrate animals assumed when stimulated in various ways (Fig. 7). Be that as it may, when Magnus with his co-worker de Kleijn demonstrated that turning of the head set up characteristic patterns of tonic reflexes (1912), Sherrington was quite content to hand this theme over to them even though, two years before, he had written in his extensive study of stepping and standing: 'Again, active or passive rotation of neck on its long axis in the decerebrate preparation inhibits extensor tonus in hind-limb on the side of the lowered pinna and causes active flexion of knee; and does so after severance of both cranial 5ths and both octavi.' Indeed, Magnus and de Kleijn were urged by Sherrington to pursue their work and in the end they made a monumental contribution to our knowledge of postural reflexes. In due course Magnus and de Kleijn became serious candidates for the Nobel prize (Liljestrand) but Magnus' untimely death (1927) put an end to such proposals.

The work of Magnus and de Kleijn is a model of pure integrative physiology. It describes a large number of automatic reflex adjustments of posture which are static 'figures' or else sequences of co-ordinated acts, the most interesting being the righting reflexes analysed in the thalamic rabbit and those arising from the labyrinthine organs and the neck muscles (or, rather, their ligaments, McCouch) which lead to characteristic postural effects from the head upon body and limbs. These involve the long spinal paths which Laslett and Sherrington had studied (1903). Magnus and de Kleijn were also inspired by their own findings to make a fundamental analysis of the natural stimuli to which the vestibular organs are sensitive, a field in which another pupil of Sherrington's, the late Mario Camis, professor at Parma, had much success. His excellent monograph *The Physiology of the Vestibular Apparatus*, was translated into English by R. S. Creed in 1930.

The integrative line and Sherrington's work on the cortex appealed particularly to pupils of certain temperaments and interests especially, of course, to those who wanted to devote themselves to clinical work; the spinal cord work, as the years went by, tended to become more theoretical and analytic and this line therefore held out greater promise for the physiologists and the theoretically minded. To the former group belonged John Fulton (1899–1960), professor at Yale University, who played a great rôle as an inspiring force in brain physiology. 'The establishment of the first laboratory of primate physiology in the U.S.A. was a signal triumph' for Fulton, wrote Earl Walker in his obituary and continued: 'experiments by the great workers of the past were repeated there under more ideal conditions and with anatomical controls so that they yielded more "meaningful" results.' In the thirties Fulton's laboratory attracted a large number of young neurologists and neurosurgeons from all over the world and many more have sought information about the intricate functions of the brain from his *Physiology of the Nervous System*. Throughout his life, Fulton looked upon the Oxford years and the guidance of Sherrington as his main source of inspiration.

The most important clinical schools which owe allegiance to Sherrington are the Montreal Neurological Institute, Wilder Penfield's creation, where he and Herbert Jasper have for years played a leading rôle in world neurosurgery, and the department of Denny-Brown in Boston, combining experimental neurology with clinical work.

A large part of the influence of a teacher, and the most difficult part to account for, derives from the example he sets in trying to realize his ideals, scientific, personal, moral, aesthetic, and in his loyalty towards them. A modicum of idolatry on the part of pupils must perhaps be accepted as an expression of their attempts to formulate valid ideals of their own, needed to carry them through disappointment and monotony. In this wider sense Sherrington was a teacher of many young men who later in life remembered him with gratitude and paid homage to his influence. These are difficult to trace unless they were actual co-workers or have since made a name for themselves in the wider subject of medicine. It is impossible to mention more than a few, neurologists such as Russell (since, Lord) Brain, Stanley Cobb, W. C. Gibson, Gordon Holmes, Sir G. Jefferson, S. Obrador, Henry Viets, F. M. R. Walshe; physiologists, as H. C. Bazett, N. B. Dreyer, Lord Florey, the brothers H. E. and E. C. Hoff, Grayson McCouch, Ian Marcou, Karl Matthes, F. R. Miller, J. M. D. Olmsted, R. W. Reid, H. E. Roaf, T. C. Ruch, K. Sassa, S. C. M. Sowton, F. M. Tozer, and many others.

Graham Brown, representing an older generation of co-workers, is here chosen as their spokesman: 'It was to those who worked in his laboratory that Sherrington gave and showed most. The research student would enter it, timidly, with a mental picture of the author of the *Integrative Action* as a man who must dwell in a sphere of his own making, difficult to attain or to travel in—a man necessarily aloof and out of common reach, "academic", coldly intellectual. But the disarming spirit of equality with which the recruit was received at once destroyed a mental barrier which could not in any case have for long withstood the sympathetic friendship which was offered by Sherrington and earned in return. . . . The laboratory life was a continuing adventure with always widening horizons . . . he would be moved . . . by the beauty of an experiment or of an ingenious technical method. And always there was originality and insight.'

Chapter 5

End-organs, Nerve Impulses and Nerve Cells

A change of scene took place when the vacuum tube made amplification of small electrical changes possible (see p. 58) and the triumphant progress of modern electronics gradually came to be reflected in nerve physiology. The pioneer whose work had the greatest immediate influence on the development of Sherrington's world of ideas was E. D. (since, Lord) Adrian. He and Sherrington were following convergent lines in the sense that both were heading for the properties of the nerve cell as a functional unit. The effect of Adrian's work was soon felt in the better understanding of the nature of the afferent message from sense organs. With several co-workers, among the best known, D. W. Bronk, Rachel Matthews, B. H. C. (since, Sir Bryan) Matthews and Yngve Zotterman, Adrian availed himself of the possibility of amplifying the small electrical changes that corresponded to the passage of impulses in individual afferent nerve-fibres and showed that the sense organs from which they emanated delivered a message coded in terms of a variation of frequency of discharge.

The individual impulse or 'spike' was the well-known action current which now became recorded as an action potential charging the grid of a vacuum tube. It was then stepped up by amplification about a million times in order to deliver the current or potential difference necessary for driving recording instruments. Fig. 14 shows that impulses at the ordinary recording speeds (used in nerve physiology) look like spikes because they are very fast. In any given nerve-fibre they do not vary in size (as the all-or-none law had correctly predicted) but merely in frequency so that the stronger the sensory stimulus, the greater the frequency at which a sense organ tends to discharge. 'The sensory messages,' said Adrian, 'are scarcely more complex than a succession of dots in the Morse code.'—'How complex must not the central processes then be in order to explain the workings of our mind,' was Sherrington's first comment.

The loudspeaker introduced by Adrian and Bronk made the repetitive discharge of individual nerve impulses more realistic and soon it became impossible to stay aloof if one was interested in sense organs. Adrian in his books, two slender volumes, described the new findings in a most enticing manner: 'The advent of the triode valve, or vacuum tube amplification,' he

Fig. 14 Discharges in dorsal cutaneous nerves of a frog. (a) shows large rapid impulses due to touching the skin; (b) slow impulses produced by 2 per cent acetic acid on the skin. (Adrian, *The Mechanism of Nervous Action*, University of Pennsylvania Press: Clarendon Press, Oxford, 1932)

said, 'has so altered the whole position that we can compare ourselves to a microscope worker who has been given a new objective with a resolving power a thousand times greater than anything he has had before. We have only to focus our instrument on the field to find something new and interesting.' This was quite true and who could refuse a peep down the tube?

In those days a key-word like 'information' was not yet used in the scientific sense it has since acquired from binary Boolean algebra. One was therefore more likely to speak of impulse patterns in single nerve-fibres and think of them as coding information from sense organs or as eliciting muscle action potentials at end-plates of muscles. Cable theory had played some rôle in the development of nerve physiology and so one was used to the idea of nerve-fibres being cables joining cells across synapses. Clearly the impulses in the nerve-fibres represented the language in which one cell speaks to another.

From now we move on familiar ground and need not discuss technical details. For some forty years impulses have been recorded from innumerable single cells and single nerve-fibres, in vertebrates and invertebrates, and much of what we know about the nervous system has come from impulse recording. Lord Adrian began his work with sensory or afferent impulses and today it still seems to me true to say that no other branch of vertebrate nerve physiology has gained as much from this technique as the study of sense organs including the projections of their afferents in the central nervous system. The eye, the ear, and the muscle spindles stand as the greatest gainers. In the twenties everything we knew about sight and hearing belonged to the realm of psychophysics. Probable functions and interpretations of histological features of the eye and the ear were deduced from psychological entities such as colour, pitch, threshold quantities of perception, etc. In spite of such limitations many brilliant discoveries had been made, especially in vision and audition, and to this very day these have guided electrophysiological research into the mechanisms that serve as cues for psychological interpretation.

From the point of view of Sherrington's earlier work the sense organs in the muscle were the most interesting ones because there was no relevant psychophysical science to tell us about the properties of the length-meters and tension-meters that he had postulated. To be sure, there was an old literature, mostly in German, about 'Kraftempfindungen' but already at the time good reason could be adduced for locating the appropriate end-organs at the joints (their ligaments). The only hope for advance lay in objective methods of recording the messages from the muscular end-organs themselves. This method was destined to solve many of the riddles that Sherrington faced when he tried to understand the interrelations between proprioceptive impulses and muscle tone. A separate chapter (7) will be devoted to these questions.

Let us now recall that a large fraction of Sherrington's experimental life had been spent in quest of the neurone. In this field he was greatly rewarded when in 1929 Denny-Brown

Plate 5 Santiago Ramòn y Cajal. (From Sherrington's obituary in *Obit. Notes Roy. Soc.*, 1935, No. 4)

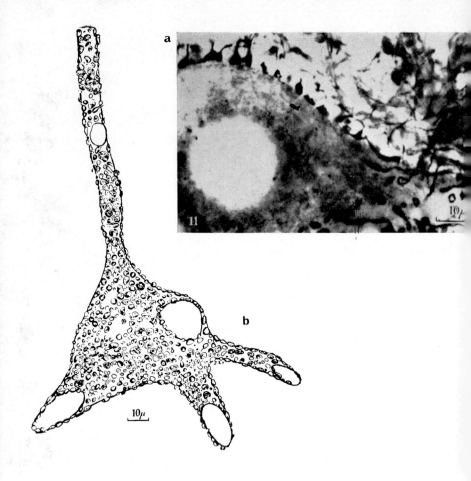

Plate 6 (a) Neurone of the ventral horn (motoneurone) of the thoracc
lumbar region of the cat (Cajal's block silver method). Fixed with formo
embedded in carbo-wax. Note the end-feet, stained deep black, along th
margin of the cell. The afferent terminals from which they originate ai
broken. (b) The motoneurone surface. *Camera lucida* drawing of part of
neurone from the ventral horn of a cat. Fixed with formol, postchrome
embedded and sectioned in carbo-wax and stained with Bielschowsk
Gros stain. The surface of the cell body and dendrites is almost entire
covered with terminal end-feet. (Wyckoff and Young, *Proc. Roy. Soc*
1955, *B144*, 440)

in his own laboratory and Adrian and Bronk at Cambridge independently demonstrated that the motor neurone — his final common path—behaves like a sense organ and fires all-or-none spikes at frequencies which increase when afferent stimulation becomes more intense. Many other facts of importance were unearthed in those papers but the fundamental analogy between sensory end-organs and neurones is of especial significance.

'The most remarkable point which arises from this paper,' said Adrian and Bronk, 'is that the discharge of a motor nerve cell can scarcely be distinguished from the discharge of a sense organ. . . . Clearly more work must be done before we can accept the view that all nervous messages are of the same general type, but some of the consequences of this view may be pointed out. In the first place it would mean that we must abandon the idea that central inhibition can be explained on the lines suggested by Lucas, Forbes, and Adrian, i.e. by the depressant effects produced by high-frequency impulse discharge. Various heroic assumptions might overcome the difficulties which would arise, but they are scarcely worth making. We must therefore revert to the view that two qualitatively different processes can occur in the synapses to account for the inhibitory and excitatory effect.' Adrian and Bronk, of course, referred to Sherrington's ideas about the central excitatory and inhibitory states, discussed in previous chapters.

The recording of impulses in single motor neurones may not seem much of a feat to the young electrophysiologists of today who have so many means of solving the technical problems involved, but an older generation of workers need not search their memories for very long to remember the situation in the mid-twenties. The existence of reflex muscle action potentials was, of course, well known. There were, for instance, Miss Florence Buchanan's (1907) studies of strychnine spasms in frogs with the aid of the capillary electrometer, and Piper's extensive work in Germany (1912) on voluntary contraction in man for which he used the Einthoven string galvanometer. Miss Buchanan had continued her teacher's work at Oxford (Sir John Scott Burdon Sanderson). Many others had followed in their path with contributions which described the electrical oscillations obtainable from the surface of contracting muscle—

8

the electromyogram—among them Dusser de Barenne, Adrian and Cooper, Paul Hoffmann, Preisendörfer, and Wachholder. Rhythms of frequencies up to 500 per sec. had been observed but it is clear, in the light of what we know today (and had reasons to suspect at the time), that these results could merely prove the existence of impulses in the muscles as electrical interference phenomena whose individual components were unknown. Von Kries, in 1923, had summed up the situation in the statement that 'for skeletal muscle we now regard the rhythmic nature of the motor innervation as certain'.

Rather dominant in the discussion was the so-called Piper rhythm, large waves at approximately 50 per sec. seen in voluntary contraction, and much worry was caused by the absence of electrophysiological signs of activity in tonic contractions until small oscillations were described independently by Dusser de Barenne and Buytendijk; in fact, one used to speak of the 'Dusser de Barenne-Buytendijk vibrations'. Little is to be gained now by discussing forgotten disputes and interpretations of tone. This brief impression from memory should suffice to give an idea of the background against which the new results stood out as revelations.

In order to interpret the Dusser de Barenne-Buytendijk vibrations in the tonically contracting soleus muscle of the decerebrate cat, Denny-Brown used the established technique of leading off from muscle but started cutting down the efferent roots cautiously until he finally had a preparation in which one or two single spikes or muscle action potentials responded by firing when the soleus was pulled out slowly. This is illustrated in Fig. 15. Now here was the stretch reflex visualized in terms of the output of a single motoneurone and with this preparation Denny-Brown made two fundamental observations. One was the curious fact that although he pulled harder and harder on the muscle, the functionally isolated motoneurone fired at much the same frequency. Yet there was every reason to assume (Adrian and Zotterman) that the muscular end-organs would stimulate their motoneurones at increasingly higher discharge frequencies. Why was this effect not reflected in the rate of firing of the motoneurone? The other new result consisted in a full vindication of the correctness and value of Sherrington's concept of recruitment. As the muscle was extended, fresh motoneurones were 'recruited' into activity (as a rule it was impossible to cut down the efferent root to one fibre only).

The Dusser de Barenne-Buytendijk vibrations now lost their relevance as a specific muscular accompaniment of tone because it was evident that they were merely the sign of a highly asynchronous reflex discharge of motoneurones, recorded in the ordinary way as muscle action potentials. The individual moto-neurones were found to discharge at very slow rates, from 5 to 25 impulses per sec. The asynchronism and slow recruitment of fresh motoneurones simply gave a low-voltage interference picture beyond the resolving power of the string galvanometer, as used in combination with non-selective recording. The

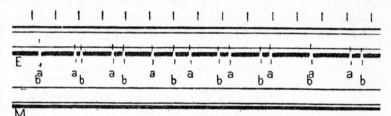

Fig. 15 Electrical response (impulses) in two soleus motor units of the decerebrate cat. The muscle is under a steady slight pull to deliver the stretch reflex shown by the activity of units *a* and *b*. The former fires seven times a second, the latter five to five and a half times a second. Time 0·1 sec. (Denny-Brown, *Proc. Roy. Soc.*, 1929, *B104*, 252)

unknown *x* that still remained to be explained concerned the regulative processes by which the motoneurones were held in check and forced to fire at such slow steady rates independent of extension in stretch. In defining recruitment Sherrington had assumed that the recruiting reflex fought its way against inhibition because pull on the muscle would mobilize both excitatory and inhibitory end-organs. Thus their rivalry would determine the outcome. While this is true, it is not a sufficient explanation of the observed stabilization of the rate of firing because recruitment was there to prove that excitation got the upper hand during increasing pull on the muscle. Stabilization must therefore be something connected with firing as such from a motoneurone, and we shall return to this point in Chapter 7. Technical improvements, which made both muscular end-organs in the periphery, and motoneurones at their sites within the spinal cord, directly accessible to analysis, in the end supplied the full explanation of stabilization of discharge rate in tone.

Adrian and Bronk had started with the phrenic nerve to the diaphragm. This supplied for study a rhythmically recurring 'natural' event. The frequency of respiratory discharge in individual motor fibres was found to be from 25 to 30 impulses per sec. in normal breathing, rising to 50–80 per sec. in forced respiration when sometimes motoneurones also began to fire in synchrony. They went on to investigate a large number of reflexes, confirming Denny-Brown's observations on the stretch reflex of the decerebrate animal, and, in general, finding rates of discharge which were adapted to the contractile properties of the muscles on which the motor fibres terminate. Rates below 50 per sec. were typical for maintained contractions but initially the frequency of discharge—just as in sense organs—might be twice that rate. Reflex action was found to be graded both by the frequency of discharge and by the number of motoneurones mobilized, the stretch reflex being unique in mainly employing a variation of number alone, as described above.

Adrian and Bronk's introduction of the concentric needle electrode for recording the muscle action potentials in voluntary contraction in man became of considerable clinical importance. Wachholder (1923) in Germany had continued Piper's work and replaced the pad leading off from the surface by two needles thrust into the contracting muscle. With this technique, making use of feeble contractions, he had seen individual muscle action potentials. With stronger contractions an oscillatory inter-ference picture was obtained. When Adrian and Bronk, by cutting down the nerve and recording from functionally isolated fibres, had proved that the efferent message did not differ in principle from its afferent counterpart, they went back to the old method of picking up the reflex efferent message after it had been translated into muscle action potentials at the motor end-plate. Their new electrode consisted of an injection needle (of the kind used with a syringe) whose shield was earthed while from the inside protruded the bared tip of a thin wire enamelled for insulation and connected to the grid of the amplifier. Single spikes were obtained between tip and shield, and by this technique they could satisfy themselves that the complex

oscillatory responses characterizing strong voluntary contractions were merely caused by the activity of more and more fibre
groups. Sherrington's concept 'motoneurone' had now been
subjected to rigorous tests and emerged unscathed.

'Reading some of the early papers of that time,' said Adrian,
'one cannot help remembering what a pleasure it was to find
that most of the inferences had been correct. Impulses arising
in sense organs or nerve cells were accompanied by action
potentials like those in a nerve trunk stimulated electrically.
They followed the all-or-nothing rule inferred from Keith
Lucas' work on the frog's dorso-cutaneous muscle. They
appeared where and when we had reason to expect them, in
sensory and in motor nerve. In fact there was no need to revise
the accepted theories of the nature of nervous communication.
It was carried out by impulses of the familiar type' (1953).
However, the insight into function that the new techniques
gradually engendered was new, and from now on the discharging cell was destined to receive an ever increasing share of the
attention of nerve physiologists. By different means Sherrington
and Adrian had been striving to make the nerve cell an analytical
unit. This had been, as I said above (p. 29), Sherrington's
'first great notion' and for him, in a sense, it was journey's end.
In 1932 Adrian and Sherrington shared the Nobel prize.

In speaking of nerve impulses in a single fibre being translated into muscle-action potentials across the motor end-plates
which it innervates, nothing has so far been said of the highly
specialized end-plate structure. This is really a synapse, located
in the periphery instead of within a centre, and much of
our basic information on synapses has come from the detailed
study of events at the motor end-plate. The fast spike in the
nerve-fibre is there translated into a slow electrical change, the
end-plate potential (Göpfert and Schaefer, 1938), which in its
turn is responsible for the muscle spike. For the understanding
of synaptic events the motor end-plate proved to be a touch-
stone making possible a decision between the two leading
theories of synaptic transmission, the chemical and the electrical
hypothesis. As briefly alluded to above, the late Otto Loewi of
Graz in Austria had shown, in a series of papers from 1921
onwards, that the effect on the heart of the two nerves, the
vagus and the accelerans, which, like the rein and the whip,

control its rhythm, is produced by two chemical mediators, the *Vagusstoff* and the *Acceleransstoff* respectively. After the extended studies of Loewi and of Dale there could be little doubt that the *Vagusstoff* was acetylcholine. Loewi had found the *Acceleransstoff* to be an adrenaline-like substance. Along independent lines U. S. von Euler many years later—in the late forties—provided evidence which led to the acceptance of one of the candidates, noradrenaline, for the rôle of transmitter substance at sympathetic nerve-endings.

The chemical theory of synaptic excitation, based on the motor end-plate as model, became firmly established when Sir Henry Dale with G. L. (now, Sir Lindor) Brown and W. Feldberg in the early thirties showed that acetylcholine was the transmitter substance responsible for the end-plate potential. The nature of the latter has since been elucidated in detail by Bernard Katz and his co-workers but a review of their results would lead us too far away from our theme. Sherrington could not on the basis of his own findings advocate any specific theory of synaptic excitation and preferred to be non-committal. For our purposes the end-plate potential can be described as a process released by the nerve impulse in order to deliver the energy needed for setting up a muscle-action potential.

Application of this model to central synapses with the motoneurone as prototype would imply that the terminal knobs of the afferents there, too, would require a chemical mediator in order to be able to depolarize the cell to the extent of making it discharge impulses down its axon. It was fairly generally and for good reasons believed that excitation led to depolarization of the cell receiving excitatory impulses, and soon there was evidence from Sir Bryan Matthews working with D. H. Barron (1935–38) to the effect that the depolarization ensuing upon activation of motoneurones could actually be led off electrotonically from the ventral roots. ('Electrotonus' is a physiological spread of current from the cell into its axon.) The idea that a synaptic potential corresponding to the end-plate potential is produced by afferent bombardment of the ventral horn cell was also strengthened by the observations that Sir John Eccles and his co-workers made in the late forties with small electrodes stuck in among the motoneurones themselves, a technique mentioned above in connection with Lorente de Nó's studies of synaptic delay (p. 59). A focal potential corresponded to activation of motoneurones, and analysis suggested that it was of cellular origin. Graded slow potentials had also been seen by Gasser, recording from the surface of the spinal cord, and work by Bremer contributed to the canonization of the general idea of a synaptic potential (depolarization of the cell membrane) being an essential link in the excitation of nerve cell bodies (including ventral horn cells). This notion was so well founded that to Eccles it seemed natural, at the time, to elaborate an electrical theory of synaptic excitation in spite of evidence to the contrary from the motor end-plate (and from the ganglions of the vagus and the sympathetic nerves). This theory need not be reviewed here as Eccles himself abandoned it some years later (see next chapter).

Sherrington's central excitatory state (Fig. 13, p. 79) was a concept that seemed supported well enough by the observations just mentioned. Further elaboration began at the Rockefeller Institute and the new approach originated in the late Herbert Gasser's interest in the conduction velocity of nerve-fibres (p. 59). Erlanger had suggested at an early date (1927) that specificity of the sensory message might well hinge upon differentiations connected with fibre size and hence with conduction velocity. The electrical technique had undergone great advance since the early days when Gasser and Erlanger measured conduction velocities in nerve-fibres with a primitive cathode ray oscillograph. Sweep and relay circuits connected to the stimulating shock made it possible by turning a knob to start any impulse at will and to visualize the electrical events on the screen with any chosen time base. It was now possible to study the temporal course of the effect of a synchronous volley of impulses. Eccles and Sherrington had, indeed, been able to execute rather complex experiments on the timing of reflexes in the early thirties but a decade of technical advance had reduced the amount of labour involved in such work and thereby pushed the experimenters on to problems requiring great precision in stimulation and recording.

In the present era one has the impression that electronic engineering has made the technical element 'foolproof' to the extent of attracting workers to this field who are ignorant of and uninterested in conceptual developments of the kind which the physiology of the central nervous system urgently demands. Sherrington's work should serve as a perpetual reminder of the necessity of long-range planning accompanied by ceaseless attempts to penetrate experiments and results with leading ideas. In this field the life of an experimenter is too short to be spent merely on *ad hoc* notions.

Eccles and Sherrington had traced the time course of the central excitatory state (see Fig. 13, p. 79) by measuring with

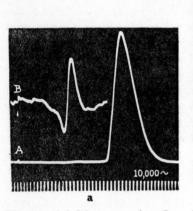 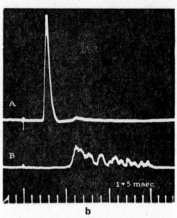

Fig. 16   (a) Monosynaptic reflex *A* recorded from the first sacral root on stimulation of the *gastrocnemius* nerves. The white mark is an artifact caused by a single electric shock, and record *B* shows when the impulse volley enters the spinal cord (on which leads have been placed). Time in 10,000 cycles per second. (b) Another similar experiment, but greater shock strength in *A* has brought in the polysynaptic reflex component from afferents of thinner calibre. *B* is a reflex to stimulation of sural nerve (a skin nerve) causing polysynaptic reflexes only. (Lloyd, *J. Neurophysiol.*, 1943, 6, 111, 293)

a test shock the effect left by a conditioning shock in the flexor centre. As defined by this experiment the time course found refers to a situation in which polysynaptic components of the afferent input have been activated and in which the relative amounts of excitatory facilitation contributed by the various neural circuits are unknown. The monosynaptic reflex made it possible to measure the time course of excitability at one specific set of synapses by the same technique (Lloyd), namely, those which represent the terminal knobs of the largest and fastest muscular afferents, as explained above (p. 65). The synchronous volley elicited in a group of such fibres undergoes little dispersion with time and finally emerges on the ventral side as the monosynaptic response illustrated in Fig. 16. Use of a weak electrical conditioning shock restricted stimulation to the largest fibres.

In agreement with Sherrington's principle of graded excitation in a 'subliminal fringe' the conditioning volley would set up an excitatory state even if the shock was too weak to excite any neurone supraliminally (above threshold). This state of facilitation would rise and fall according to some curve which the test shock would measure by the number of motoneurones (size of response) that in any given interval could be raised to firing level. Monosynaptic testing, as elaborated by Renshaw and Lloyd, is therefore a technique that depends upon the existence of a fringe of subliminally excited motoneurones. The state of facilitation obtained in this manner is seen in Fig. 17 to drop exponentially to zero in about 14 milliseconds.

The excitatory state shown in Fig. 17 is not identical with its namesake in Sherrington's conceptual world. It should preferably be called a purified version of the latter because of the weeding out of complex accessory circuits which would deliver delayed impulses capable of restoring the dwindling state of excitation. This purification of Sherrington's original concept was based on the following new analytical elements: (i) knowledge of the synaptic delay (above, p. 59); (ii) knowledge of conduction velocity of the fastest muscular afferents whose fibre size had already been measured by Sherrington in 1894; (iii) knowledge of the fact that by carefully grading stimulus strength these afferents could be selectively excited. The 'purified concept' is limited by the assumption that synchronous monosynaptic stimulation is free from specific effects depending upon the site of the monosynaptic synapses (likely to be on the cell body). Assuming that one could initiate a monosynaptic effect selectively from the dendritic portion of the motoneurone, would it follow the same curve? This point is raised merely to indicate the need for still more selective techniques (Chapter 6), which are already being employed (Fadiga and Brookhart).

It will be remembered that on Sherrington's principle of reciprocal innervation, excitation of the extensors would coincide with inhibition of the flexors and so the question arose as to whether monosynaptic excitation in one of the pair would also correspond to monosynaptic inhibition in the other. This, in fact, is what Lloyd assumed to be the case, but later work by Eccles and his colleagues has shown that inhibition is actually disynaptic. Lloyd's inhibitory curve can be roughly visualized by turning the curve of Fig. 17 by 180° around an axis formed by

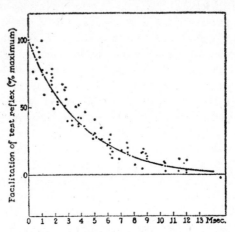

Fig. 17 The period of facilitation after a monosynaptic activation. Facilitation of motoneurones by impulses in primary afferent fibres. Points from seven experiments are scaled on the ordinates to coincide at the time of maximum facilitation. Relative facilitation, expressed in a percentage of maximum, is plotted as a function of time. The plotted curve is an exponential regression having successive half-values at 2·8, 5·6, 8·4, 11·2, and 14 msec. In four experiments, facilitation in flexor nuclei was examined; the remaining three were concerned with extensor nuclei. (Lloyd, *J. Neurophysiol.*, 1946, 9, 421)

the abscissa (see Fig. 18 (b)). For the theory of inhibition it was important at the time to possess a set of purely inhibitory monosynaptic terminals, but now, twenty years later, when inhibition has been studied by the intracellular technique (Chapter 6) in several cells of vertebrates and invertebrates, the point raised is perhaps a little academic. It created some interest because one imagined (Dale's principle) that the inhibitory and excitatory terminals of the afferent fibre, if transmission be chemical, would have to make use of the same chemical agent. For this reason it seemed natural to postulate an internuncial neurone serving as a 'commutator' to introduce a fresh set of terminals with different chemical properties specializing in inhibition. Tauc (1962) has since found that in some nerve cells of a mollusc, *Aplysia*, acetylcholine produces inhibition at some synapses, excitation at others, and, if this is verified, the effect evidently depends upon a subsynaptic elaboration at the cell membrane itself. This actually was the hypothesis that Sherrington thought most likely.

Knowledge of conduction velocity of the active fibres which proved so clarifying in the experiment just described has since served as a useful characterizing property of the type of fibres engaged and, for sensory fibres, it can only be supplanted by specifications accruing from precise use of the adequate stimulus for the end-organ itself. Unless either method of characterization of the afferent input be attempted, it is fair to say that a piece of work in this field has to offer exceptional compensations in order to possess survival value in the present age.

The relation between stimulus strength and fibre size (conduction velocity) which Gasser and Erlanger had explored so carefully suggested to Lloyd that the monosynaptic curve of facilitation (Fig. 17) could be modified by delayed excitation or inhibition in a characteristic way, depending upon stimulus strength, nature of the afferent nerve, and number of intercalated synapses, and this also proved to be the case. Examples are given in Fig. 18. Such work also led him to a general subdivision of afferent fibres into groups (Table I) according to fibre size. For the myelinated fibre in Groups I–III size is approximately proportional to conduction velocity.

TABLE I

Fibre group	I	II	III	IV
Diameter in μ	20–12	12–6	6–1	unmyelinated or C-fibres

For approximate conduction velocities in metres per second, multiply by 6.

Here was a set of specifications which has served as a useful

standard of reference in reflex work. It required knowledge of
fibre size in different afferent nerves from skin, muscles and
ligaments (in the joints), and several laboratories hastened to
contribute information of this kind (Lloyd and Chang, Rexed
and Therman, Fernand and Young, Hagbarth and Wohlfarth).
Synaptic excitation, rather than the physiological rôle of the

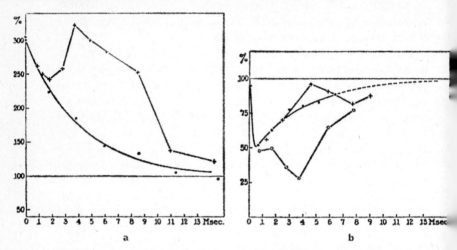

Fig. 18   (a) The period of monosynaptic facilitation has been obtained
by activating large Group I muscular afferents alone, as in Fig. 17. The
curve deviating from it at moment 2 msec. represents the effect of adding
an interneurone. This has been done by increasing stimulus strength to
include Group II afferents, i.e. by using a stronger conditioning shock.
(b) The period of inhibition by Group I afferents is represented by the
smooth curve. The secondary inhibitions and facilitations have been
obtained by activating interneurones which have afferents of lower
conduction velocity and hence have required stronger conditioning shocks.
(Lloyd, *J. Neurophysiol.*, 1946, *9*, 421)

end-organs, became the ultimate focus of that line of research
logically culminating in the intracellular studies of reflex
activity inaugurated in 1952 by Sir John Eccles and his
co-workers (Dunedin, New Zealand and then at Canberra,
Australia). From 1949 onwards my own laboratory started
pursuing questions of organization and motor control connected
with the nature of the muscular end-organs. These problems had
been neglected by the research groups interested in synaptic

transmission and in the analytical possibilities of timing central events.

In summing up the work which put conduction velocity of the afferent fibres to such good use in studies of central excitation and inhibition, let us finally consider the general question— the one that Erlanger raised—of how well specific sensory functions correlate with definite fibre groupings. To answer it, one must distinguish between statistical aspects of excitation and inhibition and the more precise correlations required to ascribe a set of fibres from one type of end-organ to one narrowly defined group of conduction velocities. In a statistical sense Lloyd's approximation, or any other classification for that matter, may often be valid and valuable as a tool in the analysis. So far it has proved most useful with the muscular afferents. But even with them there are exceptions (Bianconi and Van Der Meulen, 1962). In the ankle extensors, for instance, there is a considerable degree of overlap between fibres from tendon organs and fibres from muscle spindles with regard to conduction velocity (Hunt and Kuffler, 1951). It is also well known from the early work of Zotterman (1939) that touch is carried in both very fast and very slow fibres. In recent times Yves Laporte's group at Toulouse has devoted special attention to the relation between fibre size and function in the limb nerves. Gasser himself (1943) always advocated some caution in inferring from conduction velocity to specific sensory effects.

It remains a moot point why Sherrington, who was so interested in sense organs and at the turn of the century wrote those excellent summaries of the early work in this field in Schäfer's *Text-Book*, never himself contributed more than one study of sensory functions (as apart from end-organ anatomy), the last chapter in his *Integrative Action* dealing with fusion of binocular flicker. I can suggest no other answer than that he found reflex work more profitable from the motor point of view. No doubt he was right, and moved by the notion which he also expressed in print, that definite problems ripen for attack at definite times. The developments to which this chapter has been devoted had to come before much could be done in the sensory field. I can, however, testify to Sherrington's lively interest in sensory physiology, even at the time when the work on the spinal cord was remunerative beyond expectation. The Linacre

Lecture on *Muscular Activity* (quoted p. 76), is one instance, and when, in 1928, I turned up with a dominating interest in the retina, he told me that he had always wanted someone specializing on vision in his laboratory. Nearly all my work on the retina was carried out during his lifetime and many letters of kind encouragement from Sherrington accompanied its progress.

Chapter 6

'Inside' Information on Synaptic Action

It is now necessary to recall for a moment Bernstein's theory of excitation (1902). The nerve membrane is permeable to potassium but has very low permeability to sodium and chloride. Sodium is present in high concentration in the extracellular fluid, potassium in the axon. The resting potential (–70 mV.) between the inside (negative) and outside of the axon would be chiefly determined by its potassium content. It is impossible here to review the extraordinary amount of experimental work that has been needed to establish these few statements (Hodgkin, Huxley, Keynes, Feng, Gerard). Bernstein's theory postulated that the action potential or impulse set up by a depolarizing electrical current is a sudden reversible increase of permeability (an increase of conductance) so that the membrane potential for a moment approaches zero. Du Bois-Reymond, discoverer of the electrical nature of the nerve impulse, had called this event the negative variation because an electrode on the outside registered a negative deflexion relative to a second electrode at the cross-section of the nerve on the passage of an impulse. In 1937 Alan Hodgkin showed that the nerve impulse actually depolarizes the membrane ahead of the excited area to an extent required for the generation of a fresh impulse in the next segment, and so the spike would travel.

J. Z. Young having drawn attention to the giant nerve-fibres of the cephalopods, whose cross-sections are fifty times larger than those of vertebrate fibres, it occurred to Hodgkin and A. F. Huxley (1939) as well as to H. J. Curtis and K. S. Cole (1942) that it might be possible with this preparation to introduce a fine electrode into the axon itself to operate against another in the extracellular fluid (or a corresponding artificial solution) and so procure direct evidence as to what actually happens across the nerve membrane during impulse initiation. They were rewarded by the unexpected discovery that the nerve-action potential exceeded the resting potential. On Bernstein's theory the action potential across the membrane ought to have gone, maximally, to zero corresponding to some 70 mV. Actually it swung 30 mV. beyond it to the positive side.

Years of exacting work finally led Hodgkin and Huxley to a quantitative theory of the ionic events during the nerve impulse, which is now well supported experimentally. The essential components of the ionic theory are that the sudden increase of conductance elicited by the depolarizing current is a diphasic event, beginning with a transient sodium permeability and changing to a potassium permeability in the falling phase of the spike (or action potential). During the first phase, positive sodium ions from the outside flow into the axon and this process is recorded as the rising spike. In the second phase, the transient sodium conductance is replaced by the potassium conductance during which potassium ions move outward down their concentration gradient. The mechanisms responsible for producing and timing the exchange of the two ionic events are unknown, but the sodium conductance increases explosively when the membrane has been depolarized to a certain threshold value.

Evidence has been presented to the effect that, when an impulse is generated in motoneurones or at the motor end-plate, this process is actually preceded by a slow depolarization. As to sense organs, the author long ago postulated that 'generator potentials' would arise in them as a sequence to an initial process possessing specific sensitivity to the adequate stimulus (for instance, a photochemical reaction in the retina). Such generator potentials have since been recorded in several sensory end-organs, but it would carry us far beyond Sherrington's influence on nerve physiology to review this work.

Our present concern is with the intracellular recording from motoneurones. In the hands of Sir John Eccles and his colleagues, especially J. S. Coombs, D. R. Curtis, and P. Fatt, this has proved very rewarding and has clarified many of the problems raised in the previous chapters. This method was an offshoot of the 'inside' approach initiated by Hodgkin and Huxley. It pre-

Plate 7 Emblem on the wall of the Lecture Theatre of the Thompson-Yates Laboratories at Liverpool, stated by Sherrington to represent *Pathologia* and *Physiologia* (see text). (By courtesy of Professor R. A. Morton, Liverpool)

Plate 8 Sherrington, the Liverpool years. (By courtesy of Professor R. Gregory, Liverpool)

supposed the improvement of the microelectrode technique for which Graham and Gerard (1946) and Ling and Gerard (1949) were responsible. They had found that micro-capillaries with tips below 0·5 μ could be used to penetrate the membrane of muscle fibres and thus to record the resting potential from the inside. Nastuk and Hodgkin (1950) improved the electronics of the pick-up and succeeded in recording the muscle-action potential intracellulary.

Consider now the situation in which the experimenter attempts to obtain inside records from motoneurones. The micro-capillary must be cautiously advanced through the exposed spinal cord by some kind of micro-driver. Fixation of the preparation must be perfect. In the cat, used exclusively by Eccles and his co-workers, the average diameter of the ventral horn cells rarely exceeds 50 μ. This would provide a good target if the cells could be viewed under a microscope but, since they are deep down in the cord, the large majority of them will be by-passed or marginally wounded. In the latter case they would be incapable of maintaining their membrane potentials for more than a few seconds or minutes. With technically perfect penetrations, cells are found to retain both membrane and action potential at values near the theoretical maximum for up to an hour or more. Such cells must be reasonably normal. On the other hand, there are many experiments such as those concerning the nature of the projections on a motoneurone and its general type of response, excitatory or inhibitory to a given stimulus, which can be carried out with slightly abnormal cells. Questions may also be proposed, the answers to which can be obtained satisfactorily in a couple of minutes, before the cell has had time to deteriorate.

In order to identify a cell as a motoneurone, antidromic or backward stimulation of a ventral root is maintained at a suitable rate, and guidance for directing the search is sought in the field potential which arises with synchronous antidromic activation of a large number of motoneurones. A cathode ray oscillograph is used to display the amplified changes of potential and a loud-speaker to make them audible. When the microelectrode penetrates the cell membrane, there is a shift of base line by, optimally, some — 70 mV. (equal to the resting potential across the membrane). At the same time the small action potential,

9

of the order of a few millivolts, that had been recorded just outside the cell becomes enormous by comparison and positive, because from the new base line of, say, — 70 mV. it goes to zero by producing +70 mV. and adds a positive 'overshoot' of some 20 to 30 mV., as explained above for the axon of the squid. These events are illustrated in Plate 11. Each antidromic spike is accompanied by a sharp report from the loudspeaker adding a dramatic touch to the proceedings. With many a successful penetration the size of the spike improves for a while and the membrane potential gradually increases, apparently due to sealing up of initial leaks around the penetrating tip.

The figure shows that the action potential rises in two steps, an initial slower phase which has been found to be due to the antidromic impulse depolarizing the axon hillock. This suffices to generate a spike there which in turn depolarizes the rest of the cell, its soma and part of the dendrites, so that this portion also generates a spike, which is the one illustrated. Thus the tip of the microelectrode inside the soma can only 'see' the spike in the soma itself; the invasion of the axon hillock it records as an initial depolarization because the spike itself is too far away.

Thus the motoneurone, in generating an impulse, behaves in principle like the membrane of the giant axon of the squid *Loligo*, which was used by Hodgkin and Huxley in the experiments that led to the formulation of the ionic theory of excitation. This suggests that the vertebrate axon of which the cell is a specialized portion would behave in much the same fashion, and actually Bernhard Frankenhaeuser, by a special technique based on electronic control of the membrane potential in single vertebrate nerve-fibres, has been able to elaborate a quantitative theory of the ionic events responsible for the impulse in his preparation. With some changes in the values of the constants the same equation fits squid and vertebrate nerve, and in both cases an initial sodium conductance is replaced by a potassium conductance in the manner described above. The membrane is 'active' in the sense that when depolarized by a current to a certain threshold value, it becomes generative and fires off an impulse.

While many electrophysiological problems can be analysed by the intracellular technique and have been analysed in this way, only those directly concerned with synaptic action and reflexology in general can be taken up here. The obvious question to begin with, concerns the monosynaptic reflex. How, for instance, does the motoneurone respond to a shock from the Group I muscular afferents that is too weak to elicit a spike? In Fig. 19 it is seen to deliver a postsynaptic potential after a

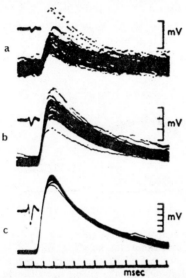

Fig. 19 Postsynaptic potentials obtained in a biceps-semitendinosus motoneurone with afferent volleys of different size. Inset records at the left of the main records show the afferent volley recorded near the entry of dorsal nerve roots into the spinal cord. They are taken with negativity downward and at a constant amplification for which no scale is given. Records are taken at an amplification that decreases in steps from (a) to (c) as the response increases. Separate vertical scales are given for each record. All records are formed by superposition of about forty faint traces. (Coombs, Curtis and Eccles, *J. Physiol.*, 1955, *130*, 374)

latent period of the order of half a millisecond during which something devoid of electrical sign happens at the synapses. The little ripple on the upper tracing is recorded with a second oscillograph beam and shows the moment at which the afferent volley enters the spinal cord. The slow response is a depolarization of the cell and Eccles has called it the 'excitatory postsynaptic potential'. This gives the time course of monosynaptic excitation and also provides an accurate measure of synaptic

delay. In previous chapters the problems were defined to which
we now have answers in intracellular terms.

Sherrington's central excitatory state, for instance, was a
graded event differing in this regard from the all-or-nothing
spike. Similarly the excitatory postsynaptic potential can be
graded in magnitude by altering stimulus strength, as shown in
the figure. The moment this potential reaches threshold value,
which in cat motoneurones takes place around 10–15 mV., the
cell fires a spike, as is illustrated in Fig. 20.

Normally the motoneurone is rarely excited by synchronous

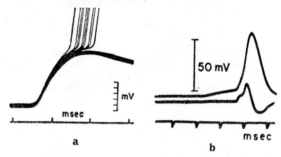

a   b

Fig. 20 (a) Postsynaptic response of a motoneurone has been recorded
intracellularly several times on standing film. The response is near
threshold and so sometimes elicits a spike action potential, sometimes not.
(b) Similar record showing spike rising from slowly augmenting postsynaptic potential. The lower record is electrically differentiated to show
rate of change of spike potential emphasizing the two phases (cf. Plate 11).
(Eccles, *The Physiology of Nerve Cells*, The Johns Hopkins University
Press, Baltimore, 1957)

volleys of the kind used in the experiments, the nearest approximation being the brief stretch reflexes of which the knee jerk is
the most familiar example. Instead there would be asynchronous
bombardment of the membrane by impulses at a very large
number of synapses and most of them would be arriving poly-
synaptically across internuncial cells. This is easily understood
when it is realized that for a total of 375,000 neurones in one
segment (the seventh lumbar segment in the dog), the numbers
of interneurones and motoneurones are related as 30 to 1
(Gelfan, 1963). Several counts have been made of the average
number of synapses on a motoneurone. A generally accepted
figure is 2,000 (Barr, Wyckoff and Young) but for the largest

motoneurones with a diameter of 65 μ, Gelfan gives an estimated figure of 10,000 synapses, of which a mere one-third would be on the cell body, the rest on the dendrites. One has to imagine, therefore, that the normal activity of a motoneurone is maintained by a large number of polysynaptic impulses arriving in temporal dispersion to build up the central excitatory state by summation.

Synchronous monosynaptic activation, though in itself slightly

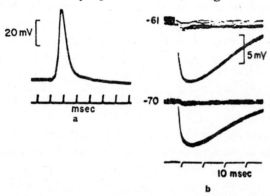

Fig. 21 (a) The intracellularly recorded antidromic response of a motoneurone. Note the 'after-hyperpolarization' which succeeds the spike and which is a slow increase of membrane potential (downward swing in record). (b) The after-hyperpolarization is separately recorded here, greatly magnified, and with the time-base slowed down to display its duration. On the right are given the values of the membrane potentials in the two cases. Note that the spike would be too large and too much compressed to be visible at this magnification and time scale. (Eccles, *The Physiology of Nerve Cells*, The Johns Hopkins University Press, Baltimore, 1957)

artificial, has proved valuable as an experimental approach (cf. Lloyd's work, reviewed in Chapter 5), because it illustrates in a purified state and magnified by synchrony the properties of the synaptically activated motoneurone membrane unmodified by delayed impulses from sources beyond control. Monosynaptic reflexes have also been used as standard tools in the analytical work of Eccles and his colleagues. One of their major findings is the after-hyperpolarization following the spike, illustrated in Fig. 21. This is a slow swing of potential towards values below the base-line. It had previously been studied in peripheral nerves by Gasser and there found to be accompanied by a parallel reduction of excitability. In the motoneurone after-hyperpolarization is far more prominent than in its axon. Since it represents an increase of the membrane potential, a repolarization, it is accompanied by a reduction of excitability. Taking a concrete example, assume that the membrane potential had been — 70 mV. at the outset and that the spike momentarily had reduced it to $70+30=100$ mV., after-hyperpolarization might have carried it to — 75 mV. at the lowest point of the slow change illustrated in Fig. 23. Motoneurones differ a great deal among themselves with respect to duration and amount of after-hyperpolarization, and this, as we shall see, is important for the understanding of variations in firing rate (Chapter 7), because evidently firing levels of depolarization have to be re-established by temporal summation from the initial position at the end of the spike.

Much information has been obtained by using two stimulating shocks at varying intervals. In the experiment, analysed in Fig. 22, the first shock is antidromic and hence non-synaptic. It merely serves to set up a spike. The second shock is orthodromic (afferent) by the monosynaptic route. The question raised by this arrangement of the stimuli is: how soon after the discharge of an impulse is the motoneurone prepared to deliver an excitatory postsynaptic potential? It was found by Coombs, Curtis, and Eccles that the postsynaptic potential is diminished for several milliseconds after the antidromic spike and that at an interval of about 1·2 msec. it is practically non-existent. This also means that, if the orthodromic impulse is prevented from generating a synaptic potential for 1·2 msec., it cannot do so at all and therefore the depolarizing activity at the synapse itself cannot have lasted any longer. In Fig. 23 (a), the process of activation itself is shown by the broken line. The monosynaptic postsynaptic potential is traced by the line drawn in full. In Fig. 23 (b), there is a graphic presentation of the subsynaptic currents generated by the activation of one synapse. In order to depolarize the cell, the current must be outwardly directed across the membrane and hence the subsynaptic current must take an inward course.

The brief bursts of subsynaptic currents at a large number of synapses may be regarded as the elementary events in synaptic excitation. There will be spatial summation at adjacent synapses forming confluence zones of subsynaptic currents. Discharge of a spike involves a tendency towards destruction of the excitatory state of depolarization but if temporal summation is operating all the time, the losses will also be filled in and so repetitive firing can be maintained.

When the membrane is depolarized by a synchronous volley, the time course of its immediate response depends upon the

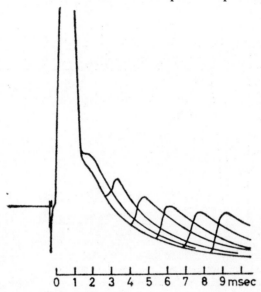

Fig. 22 Combined tracing of antidromic motoneurone action potential alone and the postsynaptic potentials obtained at various moments after it. (Eccles, *The Physiology of Nerve Cells*, The Johns Hopkins University Press, Baltimore, 1957)

product of its two electrical constants, resistance and capacity, and this is the effect that is illustrated by broken lines in Fig. 23 (a). The postsynaptic potential (line drawn in full) is a more complex affair and its time course cannot be said to be fully understood. There may be a residuum of delayed synaptic currents and probably the dendrites, to which the effect must spread from the soma or cell body of the motoneurone, respond more slowly than the latter. Be that as it may, monosynaptic excitation has the time course illustrated by its postsynaptic potential, and this is the fundamental event behind Lloyd's curve of Fig. 17 in the previous chapter. This was described as a 'purification' of Sherrington's concept 'central excitatory state' which we now find translated into a depolarizing potential of definite time course, as extracellular work had predicted.

It remains to ask if the subsynaptic currents which carry the

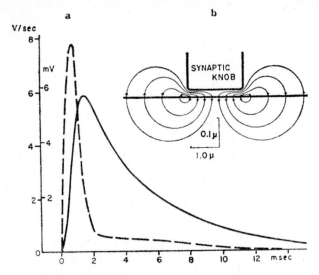

Fig. 23   (a) The unbroken line is the mean of several postsynaptic potentials in cat motoneurones, while the broken one shows the period of the subsynaptic currents required to generate this change of potential. (b) Diagram showing the subsynaptic currents during the activation of one synapse. The synaptic cleft between the knob and the membrane of the motoneurone is magnified out of scale. The current passes inwards through the subsynaptic area and outward through the cell membrane. (Eccles, *The Physiology of Nerve Cells*, The Johns Hopkins University Press, Baltimore, 1957)

ions across the cell membrane are delivered by the terminal impulse directly or whether here, too, a chemical process is fulfilling the rôle of acetylcholine at the motor end-plate. The answer will be postponed until synaptic inhibition has been discussed. The further problem as to what ions are concerned in the three changes of potential so far described, the postsynaptic potential, the spike, and the after-hyperpolarization, has been studied a great deal, mainly by Eccles and his colleagues, but it would carry us too far into theoretical electrophysiology to review this extensive work which is of little significance for the set of ideas that Sherrington fostered.

Of more direct interest from our point of view is the question of how the motoneurones function repetitively. Not only reflex behaviour but most of the problems relating to motor control (the next chapter) require knowledge of the rules by which the

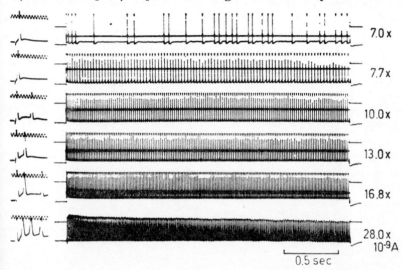

Fig. 24 Intracellular stimulation of the rat motoneurone (spike size 81 mV.) by currents of different strength. On the left, the initial spikes are recorded on a fast sweep circuit with time in msec. Note there is a change of sensitivity of the current-recording beam of the oscillograph at $7.7 \times 10^{-9} A = 7.7$ nA. For the strongest current, spike size has diminished (cf. Fig. 25 for plot). (Granit, Kernell, and Shortess, *J. Physiol.*, 1963, *169*, 743)

outward membrane current determines impulse frequency. Our laboratory (Granit, Kernell, Shortess, Smith) has been interested in this aspect of the intracellular approach which can be studied by passing an outward current through the tip of the micro-capillary, a technique devised by Araki and Otani (1955). If the tip of the electrode is made positive, current will pass through the membrane to the outside negative electrode, and it is then possible to measure impulse frequency as a function of depolarizing current strength in nA. ($=10^{-9}$ Amp.), a fair imitation of how an asynchronous barrage of impulses at the terminals will depolarize the cell. The result of such an experiment is shown in Fig. 24. It is evaluated graphically in Fig. 25,

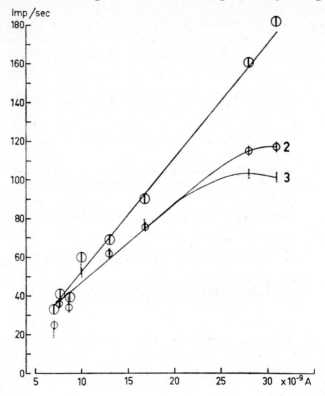

Fig. 25 Frequency of discharge plotted against current strength for the motoneurone of Fig. 24. Curve 1 shows a constant slope of 5·9 impulses per sec. per nA and is derived from the 0·3 sec. following the first interval; curve 2, the same after 1·3 sec.; curve 3, the same after 2·6 sec. with the measuring time extended to 0·5 sec. The slope constant of 2 and 3 is 4·1 impulses per sec. per nA. (Granit, Kernell, and Shortess, *J. Physiol.*, 1963, *169*, 743)

the frequency of discharge being plotted against current strength.

Clearly the relation between current intensity and rate of firing is linear within the range of normal frequencies of discharge. There is also a process of 'adaptation' implying that the slope of the curve is steep at the onset of stimulation and within half a second or so acquires a steady or 'adapted' value characterized by a smaller slope constant. In tonically firing motoneurones, which can be kept discharging for a long time, 'adapted' slope constants are around 2·5 impulses per sec. per nA. Some neurones refuse to fire more than a brief burst to inside stimulation, whatever the current strength. In such cases the relation between spike frequency and current intensity is also linear but the slope constant is high and adaptation so fast that motoneurones of this type, if assumed to be normal, could only take part in phasic responses. The 'adaptive process' implies that the membrane of the motoneurone exerts a stabilizing effect on the rate of discharge, and close inspection of the records of Fig. 24 shows that an important rôle in tonic firing is also played by after-hyperpolarization which initially gradually improves during maintained intracellular stimulation.

The experiments just described may also be regarded as attempts at defining the 'amplification factor' of the motoneurone. The slope is a measure of this. Initially, when the slope of the curves relating rate of firing to current strength is high, the motoneurone is a very efficient amplifier of the input, and those motoneurones which are restricted to the firing of initial bursts will always operate in this manner. Most sense organs can start firing at high rates and are then also sensitive to rate of change of stimulation, after which those capable of responding tonically settle down by adaptation to a lower maintained frequency of discharge. Motoneurones and end-organs are therefore well matched to respond both to rate of change and to maintained stimulation.

So far the discussion has only been concerned with excitation in motoneurones, but the intracellular approach has been extended to both interneurones and a great many different nerve cells in various invertebrates, all of which have been found to generate postsynaptic potentials in response to stimulation. Interneurones in the spinal cord are of considerable interest for the understanding of all problems of motor control, and the so-called Renshaw cell will here be chosen as their prototype (Eccles, Fatt, and Koketsu, 1954).

Renshaw cells were discovered in 1946 by the late Birdsey Renshaw who fired a volley antidromically into a ventral root while fine electrodes had been thrust into the spinal cord in the neighbourhood of the motoneurones for recording. He then found cells which fired to a single shock in the manner illustrated in Fig. 26 (b). The initial frequency is extremely high, 1,000 to 1,500 impulses per second for the first pair of spikes, the rate of firing then petering out in the manner illustrated. The discharge followed after a brief latent period and its changing rate of discharge was imitated by a depression of monosynaptic reflex excitability which started rapidly and slowly diminished. The reflex excitability was studied by monosynaptic testing (Chapter 5), for which one portion of a ventral root was used, while the rest of the root served for antidromic stimulation.

When the Canberra group returned to this problem they were able to demonstrate that, corresponding to the discharge of the Renshaw cells, the motoneurones became repolarized for some forty milliseconds along a curve whose depth, just like the monosynaptic depression, reproduced the time course of rate of firing in the Renshaw cells. This curve, together with the circuit diagram (Fig. 26 (c)) that was suggested by the results, is shown in Fig. 26 (a). The axons of the motoneurones were actually found by Golgi to possess branches, called recurrent collaterals, which return to the grey matter of the spinal cord. In the diagram these have synapses on the Renshaw cells which in their turn repolarize the motoneurones. This detour gives the circuit its latent period. The ensuing repolarization will augment after-hyperpolarization but while the latter is in sequence to the spike, and therefore restricted to the firing cell, recurrent repolarization is caused by synapses which the Renshaw cells establish by their terminals converging upon a large number of motoneurones (Szentágothai, 1956). By definition, the effect is therefore an inhibition. Antidromic or recurrent inhibition at the cell membrane thus appears as a postsynaptic potential of opposite sign relative to its excitatory counterpart. Actually, this was not the first example of a postsynaptic inhibition that Eccles and his co-workers encountered, but it is a particularly lucid case because here we possess both the circuit diagram as well as the firing of the internuncial cells.

How definite is the evidence for the synaptic nature of antidromic inhibition? Could it not be a depression exerted by currents spreading from adjacent motoneurones activated anti-

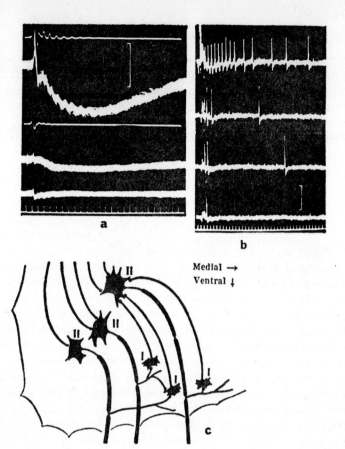

Medial →
Ventral ↓

Fig. 26 (a) Intracellular recording from a biceps-semitendinosus motoneurone. The potential simultaneously recorded by a surface lead on the dorso-lateral aspect of the spinal cord is shown above the first two intracellular records. The main curves show, reading from top to bottom, hyperpolarizations produced by antidromic volleys in the biceps-semitendinosus and in the semimembranosus motor axons, while the lowest record shows zero effect of a plantaris antidromic volley. The motoneurone was not invaded antidromically by the impulse in its own motor axon, so in the uppermost record there is no complication by the positive after-potential. All records are made by the superimposition of about forty faint traces to eliminate random noise. Time in msec.: potential scale, 5 mV. (b) The upper record shows the rhythmic response set up in an interneurone by an antidromic volley in the biceps-semitendinosus motor axons. Other records, going downward, are responses of the same interneurone elicited by antidromic volleys in the motor axons to *gastrocnemius, flexor longus digitorum,* and the deep peroneal group of muscles respectively. Time in msec.: potential scale, 0·5 mV. (c) Circuit diagram showing motoneurones (II) with their axons and recurrent collaterals which run to Renshaw cells (I). The latter have inhibitory synapses on the motoneurones. (Eccles, Fatt, and Koketsu, *Aust. J. Sci.,* 1953, *16,* 50)

dromically? Such arguments which had to be considered when Renshaw published his observations need not be taken too seriously today. At the time, depression of motoneurone excitability to antidromic stimulation of ventral roots was not unknown. It had been seen by Denny-Brown in 1929, and Eccles and Sherrington in the early thirties had employed antidromic stimulation of motoneurones in experiments which it would serve no purpose to review in this connection. Even recurrent collaterals had received some attention (Graham Brown, 1914, Forbes, 1933) but the time was not ripe for the handling of such problems.

What really became decisive for the new developments was the discovery of the discharge from the Renshaw cells coupled with intracellular recording from adjacent motoneurones. Eccles, Fatt, and Koketsu could then prove that the amount and duration of the repolarization of the motoneurone depended upon the strength of the antidromic shock in the same manner as did the frequency and duration of the discharge of the Renshaw cells. The latent periods of the two events also agreed with this interpretation of cause and effect. Furthermore, the discharge of the Renshaw cells and the inhibitory postsynaptic potential were both augmented and prolonged by eserine which neutralizes the esterase that normally removes acetylcholine. Remembering that the motoneurone acts by liberating acetylcholine at motor end-plates in the periphery, it seems reasonable (on Dale's principle) that the recurrent branches of the same axon also would be cholinergic and hence liberate acetylcholine at their synapses on the Renshaw cells. Other experiments with drugs also show the same close parallelism between motoneurone excitability and recurrent inhibition, and differentiate it from electrotonic effects recordable in the ventral roots (V. J. Wilson).

Eccles and his co-workers have also succeeded in obtaining some intracellular records from Renshaw cells which proved them to be depolarized by antidromic stimulation. This is the synapse that was found to be cholinergic. The nature of the postulated transmitter at the second synapse, the one established by axons from Renshaw cells on motoneurones and which causes the inhibitory postsynaptic potential, is unknown. In vertebrates, while the number of candidates for the rôle of transmitter substances at central synapses tends to increase, the finding of cholinergic excitation at the Renshaw cells by Eccles, Fatt, and Koketsu is still the best case in which identification is supported by evidence of a more substantial nature.

The inhibitory postsynaptic potential, which has been introduced here on the basis of results obtained with recurrent collaterals, was first described in 1952 by Brock, Coombs, and Eccles using the reciprocal inhibition which monosynaptic excitatory afferents exert on the motoneurones of their antagonists (cf. Chapters 3 and 5). Lloyd had called it direct inhibition

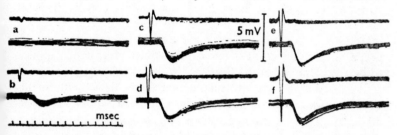

Fig. 27 Lower records give the intracellular responses of a biceps-semitendinosus motoneurone to a quadriceps volley of progressively increasing size, as is shown by the upper records which are recorded from the L6 dorsal root by a surface electrode (downward deflections signalling negativity). Note the three gradations in the size of the inhibitory postsynaptic potential; from (a) to (b), from (b) to (c), and from (d) to (e). All records are formed by the superposition of about forty faint traces. The voltage scale shows 5 mV. for intracellular records, downward deflexions indicating membrane hyperpolarization. (Coombs, Eccles, and Fatt, *J. Physiol.*, 1955, *130*, 396)

and still maintains that it is direct in the sense that it, too, is monosynaptic and thus a true adjunct to its excitatory counterpart, presented above in Figs. 17 and 19. The intracellular picture of this inhibition is given in Fig. 27. This process is also a graded postsynaptic potential but of opposite sign (repolarization) compared with the excitatory postsynaptic potential (depolarization). It differs from the latter in being delayed by the time corresponding to one synapse and for this reason Eccles and his co-workers have established an additional synapse *en route* (cf. also Lundberg). At the time it also appeared rather unlikely that the afferent fibre which has excitatory terminals on one kind of motoneurone would have inhibitory terminals on another. As pointed out in the previous chapter, this argument seemed sensible if one could assume that synaptic specificity resides in the terminals. Recently, however, Tauc (1952) has obtained evidence with the mollusc *Aplysia* which places specificity on the subsynaptic side of the membrane. In his preparation the nerve cells are visible and so can be punctured under the microscope while micropipettes can be used for direct application of acetylcholine. Some cells responded to acetylcholine with postsynaptic excitation, others with postsynaptic inhibition and in the two types corresponding effects were obtained by afferent stimulation. Since we have good reasons for concluding with Eccles that different ionic mechanisms operate in excitation and inhibition, it is of considerable theoretical interest to possess a preparation in which the chemical transmitter substance appears to be the same for both effects.

It is hardly necessary to supplement the evidence with further experiments from the work of the Canberra school and other research groups studying mono- and polysynaptic circuits in different cells and animals; it has been proved beyond doubt that excitation and inhibition are represented by postsynaptic potentials of opposite sign. The pyramidal cells (Phillips, 1956) might be added in order to include the brain, and the crustacean stretch receptor (Kuffler and Eyzaguirre, 1955) would be a good representative of a sense organ provided with an inhibitory terminal from a centrifugal nerve. In the latter, too, excitation is a depolarization and inhibition a repolarization of the cell membrane, and both events can be studied in a cell that is visible under the microscope.

After the discovery of the postsynaptic inhibitory potential the case for chemical transmission seemed very convincing. If one were to assume that the electrical impulse in the terminal would cross the subsynaptic cleft and the cellular membrane to produce the necessary subsynaptic current, how then could the same current from an otherwise identical impulse run in an opposite direction, as it would have to do in order to produce the inhibitory subsynaptic current? The chemical mediator seems, in fact, unavoidable in a system of the type which is so common in vertebrates, i.e. a small surface, like that of the synapse, faced with the task of exciting a disproportionately larger structure (cf. the motor end-plate, Chapter 5). Admittedly it has been difficult to detect chemical transmittor substances at central synapses in vertebrates, but this need not mean that such mediators do not exist. The fact (Bradley and Eccles) that postsynaptic inhibitory potentials often are antagonized by strychnine seems encouraging.

In the intracellular work on vertebrates the motoneurone has been the well-established favourite. This is because of its size and because there is a considerable amount of background knowledge about motoneurones inherited from the Sherrington epoch. If the theme of this book were not limited to tracing Sherrington's influence on nerve physiology, much space ought to have been devoted to other structures, especially to the motor end-plate, whose study in the hands of Bernard Katz has led to important conceptual advances clarifying both the electrophysiology of excitation and the mode of action of acetylcholine; but this would carry us too far into biophysics. Nevertheless it should be remembered here that the motoneurone with its synapses need not necessarily be regarded as the only possible model of synaptic organization existing in the central nervous system of the vertebrates. It has already been pointed out that the interneurones (the Renshaw cell being our prototype) behave as if the production and disappearance of the chemical transmitter substance were a much slower affair than in the motoneurone. Unfortunately we have but little information concerning the relationship between transmembrane current strength and impulse frequency for any interneurones. If their slope constants were very large, a vigorous burst of impulses would follow from a very small and brief depolarizing current.

Synapses whose transmission is based on a purely electrical mechanism have been found in invertebrates (Fursphan and Potter) and axo-axonic synapses which are known in vertebrates (e.g. in the retina) may be capable of utilizing similar principles. Chemical transmission has been demonstrated in invertebrates (Bullock and Hagiwara, and the later work by Tauc, referred to). In this field invertebrate cells often provide the experimenter with the great advantage that the preparation can be observed under the microscope. Then both pre- and postsynaptic microelectrodes can sometimes be applied.

The terms 'excitation' and 'inhibition' are also used in a more general sense to mean almost any augmentation or diminu-

10

tion of excitability in a centre. Examples will be given below. For the time being it suffices to state in conclusion that the two postsynaptic mechanisms are common throughout the whole animal kingdom.

In his intracellular work on the postsynaptic excitatory and inhibitory potentials in the spinal cord Eccles may be said to have run out the course that Sherrington set, besides adding many new and significant observations to those briefly reviewed. The concepts of Sherrington (Chapter 3) have now been verified and reformulated in terms which for postsynaptic excitation and inhibition agree almost word for word with those of the old Master's, as was pointed out by Sir John Eccles himself in a review of *Development of Ideas on the Synapse* (1959). Postsynaptic inhibition is a stabilization of the potential of the cell membrane; it can be neutralized by postsynaptic excitation, the two processes being represented by potential changes of opposite direction; both events can be subliminal from the point of view of the firing mechanism and both are capable of being nicely graded; specific sensitivity to either of the two is likely to be localized in the cellular membrane rather than at the terminals themselves, etc. One is tempted here to quote Lord Adrian's remark about his own work a second time: 'Reading some of the early papers of that time one cannot help remembering what a pleasure it was to find that most of the inferences had been correct.' Thus it seems that biological imagination counts for something when critically applied. As a lighthouse in the dark it goes on beckoning the sailor to stay on the right course.

Sherrington's early studies of reflex excitation and inhibition interacting on the same neurone had finally led him to the daring statement that 'the net change which results there when the two areas are stimulated concurrently is an algebraical sum of the *plus* and *minus* effects producible separately by stimulating singly the two antagonistic nerves' (1908). Would it really be possible, using natural stimuli, to carry out a physiological experiment on pitting inhibition against excitation in such a manner that the result would be quantitative enough for investigating this proposition? In my presentation of all these problems it has been necessary to simplify the issue a little. Actually Eccles and others have shown that the amount of inhibitory postsynaptic potential depends on the level of membrane potential being next to nothing if the latter is high, and so the algebra may go wrong with motoneurones which for some reason have high membrane potentials, for instance in the case of deeply anaesthetized animals. The decerebrate preparation therefore suggested itself as the best choice. Pure inhibitory nerves are also very rare but the recurrent circuit had been found to give regular and good inhibition on tonically discharging moto-neurones in decerebrate animals (Granit, Pascoe, and Steg) and this inhibition had been shown to be a postsynaptic repolariza-tion (see above). The experiment to be described (Granit and Renkin) employed recurrent inhibition on tonic motoneurones which had been made to fire at different rates by varying the repetitive afferent stimulus.

The experiment presupposes knowledge of the fact, demon-strated above in Figs. 24 and 25, that firing rate is directly proportional to the intensity of the depolarizing current and so can be used as a measure of the latter. A reduction of firing rate by recurrent inhibition will mean 'running down' on the same curve along which excitation is 'running up', a curve like the one in Fig. 25. If a motoneurone is being fired at different fre-quencies, then on the theory a constant recurrent inhibition, produced by repetitive antidromic stimulation of adjacent ventral root fibres, should always remove the same number of impulses. This follows simply from the fact that a constant repolarization must shift the curve of Fig. 28 downwards by a constant amount without altering its slope.

In plotting the results of such experiments it is convenient to represent the various firing rates (F_n) of the motoneurone on the abscissa and the value obtained by inhibition (F_i) on the ordinate. If there were no inhibition the two frequencies would always be identical and the plot would be the line drawn in Fig. 30 through the origin at an angle of $45°$, meaning that the proportionality constant would be 1·00. When constant recur-rent inhibition is applied, then the curve through the observed values is found shifted downwards by a constant amount and hence it, too, has a proportionality constant equal to 1·00. When the 470 observations with 18 cells were averaged and treated statistically, the proportionality constant proved to be 0·996—unexpectedly close to 1·00—and the average reduction of firing rate by inhibition 5·5 impulses per second.

In the same type of experiment and using as indicator the steady state of tonic firing of a motoneurone in the decerebrate

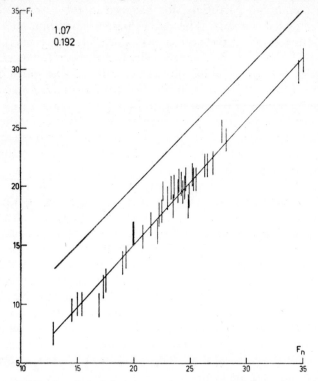

Fig. 28   Results plotted from experiments on the decerebrate cat in which a single extensor motoneurone is fired synaptically at different spike frequencies, F_n (abscissae), while the diminution of these frequencies during recurrent inhibition, maintained at rates above 50 per sec., is plotted as F_i (ordinates). The line above that drawn through the recorded values passes through the origin with a slope of 45°, meaning that in this case there would be no recurrent inhibition ($F_n = F_i$). It should be noted that during recurrent inhibition the drop in the value of F_i is independent of the rate of discharge of motoneurone, F_n. The proportionality constant is 1·07, the standard error is 0·192 impulses per sec. (Granit and Renkin, *J. Physiol.*, 1961, *158*, 461)

preparation, it seemed also worth while to investigate the effect of varying the frequency of the antidromic tetanus. (Anticipating points of view to be taken up in the next chapter, this at the same time means inquiring into the properties of negative feedback.) It was found that the effect of recurrent inhibition was proportional to antidromic stimulus frequency.

These results are of especial interest because the two rules that were established turned out to be a replica of rules valid for so-called lateral inhibition (H. K. Hartline) in the eye of the horseshoe crab *Limulus*. The recurrent effect in Hartline's preparation does not seem to involve an interneurone. The visual cells have been found to dispatch 'lateral' or recurrent fibres to one another as they leave the eye. Single adjacent visual cells can be illuminated separately and interaction studied in terms of frequency of firing as set by level of illumination. A cell firing at constant rate will by lateral inhibition remove a fixed number of impulses from a firing neighbour, whatever the discharge rate of the latter, and this inhibitory effect is proportional to the rate of firing of the inhibiting cell.

Hartline and Ratliff at the Rockefeller Institute have shown that (recurrent) lateral inhibition in the *Limulus* eye is a mechanism for emphasizing the contours, and they have also been able, with this ideal preparation, to produce a rigorous quantitative analysis of visual contrast. Let it suffice here to point out that for physical reasons the edges of a visual image would always be blurred. These would be reproduced by slowly firing cells unless their activity were suppressed by their well-illuminated neighbours firing at a fast rate. Lateral inhibition will thus enhance contours. Similarly, with tonic firing of motoneurones, the feebly activated fringe neurones will be held in check by those firing at faster rates. Recurrent inhibition will therefore produce 'motor contrast'. In the animal kingdom *Limulus* is one of the most ancient of known species. Our comparison with Hartline's work thus shows that feedback mechanisms, based on discharge rate and simple linear equations, have been preserved up to the highest level where it has been possible to make an examination of them.

After this final verification of ideas from the beginning of this century on algebraical summation of excitation and inhibition it is now necessary to consider some aspects of central excitation and inhibition that Sherrington had not thought of. 'Inhibition' in particular has been used rather loosely as a term, and it seems clear at the outset that in a complex structure such as the central nervous system, many processes may occur that would lead to a reduction or increase of excitability. A tendency in the present age of micro-analysis has been to go for the causes where previously one had to be satisfied with the effects.

Most important in this connection is the so-called post-activation potentiation (post-tetanic potentiation), known for a very long time from work on the motor end-plate. As a synaptic phenomenon it aroused fresh interest when Bronk and Larrabee in 1947 presented a careful analysis of it in the synaptic projections to a sympathetic ganglion cell. They showed that after some seconds of high-frequency stimulation of the nerves to such a ganglion, it became more responsive to a test shock given to the same fibres. There was never a rise of excitability to testing with any other fibres than those actually tetanized. The effect was therefore a kind of local 'memory' in the terminals or synapses of the fibres that had been stimulated. It might last up to five minutes.

Fundamentally similar experiments were then carried out by Lloyd with the monosynaptic circuit for the motoneurones and he also obtained the same results. Post-activation potentiation is now generally recognized as a mechanism in its own right. Partly, or perhaps even chiefly, it depends upon the fact that tetanized nerve terminals develop long-lasting hyperpolarizations. Consequently the test impulse, travelling through this region, will undergo an equivalent increase in size and so be a more efficient stimulus for the mechanism at the synapse. This explanation was originally given by Lloyd and has found general acceptance. To this should be added that the Canberra group have evidence for the destruction and re-synthesis of the chemical transmitter also being influenced by long-lasting tetani. The postactivation potentiation of this type is of shorter duration.

The presynaptic component of post-activation potentiation (hyperpolarization) is of interest for several reasons. Firstly, it brings the afferent terminals into the picture, secondly, it suggests a method of labelling certain terminals and has been used for this purpose (Granit, Lundberg), finally, it is greatly enhanced by high stimulus frequencies such as have been recorded in sensory end-organs and interneurones. It has, for instance, been shown to operate under physiological circumstances, e.g. after pull on muscles (Granit, 1956) whose stretch receptors discharge impulses at high frequencies by the mono-synaptic route. For this reason my own view is that it also plays a rôle in spasticity.

The opposite situation in which the cellular membrane is hyper-depolarized is also a theoretical possibility. This state is easily created experimentally in peripheral axons (Hodgkin and Huxley, Frankenhaeuser) where it produces diminution of spike height and in the end leads to 'inactivation' of the generative process that is initiated by depolarization. Recent work indicates that both cell body and terminal membranes have incorporated this mechanism in their fabric of controls. It was found to occur in the cerebellar Purkinje cells which may suddenly deliver a burst of spikes growing smaller and finally disappearing while the cell membrane swings in the direction of excessive depolarization (extra- and intracellular records of Granit and Phillips, 1956).

Inactivation could serve 'inhibition' in some systems and has actually been found as a regular feature in the large hippocampal neurones (C. von Euler and Green, 1960) which normally act in unison to produce slow, so-called theta waves which consist of periods of activation, inactivation and restoration of membrane potential, recently studied by the intracellular technique (Spencer and Kandel, 1962). Inactivation has also been found in several invertebrate cells, a striking example being the crustacean stretch receptor (Kuffler and Eyzaguirre, 1955). In cerebellar Purkinje cells and in the hippocampal pyramids inactivation has also been noted with extracellular recording, a point of some importance because excessive depolarization can easily occur as an artefact as a sequence to penetration of the cell membrane (Lundberg and Norrsell).

With microelectrodes stuck in among the terminals of skin afferents, Patrick Wall (1958) discovered that they underwent depolarization leading to diminution of spike height, and his technique has since been used by Eccles and his co-workers in extensive studies of this variety of 'presynaptic inhibition', a pendant to post-activation potentiation. They have shown that terminal depolarization suggests a clue to the understanding of a number of electrophysiological phenomena, but it would carry the reader too far to discuss this here, particularly since pre-synaptic inhibition has not yet been sufficiently studied with 'natural' modes of stimulation. Their most important hypothesis is that one afferent system may cause 'presynaptic inhibition' at the terminals of another, from which would follow that there might be synapses on the terminals themselves engaged in depolarizing their membranes.

Wall's findings would possibly have received scant attention had not Frank and Fuortes (1957) by the intracellular technique been able to demonstrate that 'inhibition' in the sense of a diminution of excitatory postsynaptic potentials could be obtained without change of resting membrane potential. Since postsynaptic inhibition is an increase of membrane potential, by what mechanism was this 'diminution of excitation' brought about? Frank and Fuortes called it 'remote inhibition' and Eccles identifies it with the presynaptic depolarization of the terminals, to which his group has lately devoted so much experimental work. Is the existence of real 'remote inhibition' thereby excluded and finally relegated to the realm of presynaptic depolarizations? It is too early to reply to this question in the affirmative. We know far too little about the chemical side of the synaptic mechanism, nor has pure dendritic excitation been sufficiently explored.

Historically 'presynaptic inhibition' is an offshoot of the line of thought for which Lucas became responsible when he ascribed inhibition to a blocking process such as the Wedensky inhibition at the end-plates caused by high-frequency tetanization of the motor nerve. When Gasser studied the excitability changes following trains of impulses in the peripheral nerve, he was led to think of inhibition along similar lines. Lloyd's study of the monosynaptic reflex and 'direct inhibition' may be said to have re-installed the ideas of Sherrington. Presynaptic inhibition has always had a number of talented advocates (Gasser, Matthews, Bremer, Wall) but until the advent of the intracellular microelectrode its champions have not had much of a chance to expand beyond plausibilities. And why should it not be plausible to assume that inhibition of a motoneurone could be the consequence of diminution of excitation owing to a block somewhere in the path? Assume this path to be one which projects exclusively on to the dendrites. Can we then be quite certain that the intracellular microelectrode in the soma really is capable of reflecting this distant event by an increase of membrane potential? It is also a little confusing that no sooner is a reduction of excitability observed than it is described as an 'inhibition' while corresponding increases of excitability are more correctly termed as what they are. It would perhaps be advisable to restrict the term inhibition to Eccles' postsynaptic process which has since been found in nerve cells throughout the animal kingdom.

Chapter 7

From Reflexes to Problems of Motor Control: Tone

It has been shown how the 'reflex' served as a solid stepping-stone to the understanding of problems of synaptic action once it had been correctly conceptualized and firmly tied to histology by Sherrington. But to him reflexes were more than that; they were also simple items of behaviour 'likely to reveal explicitly some basal elements fundamental to all co-ordination' though not necessarily all of them. With the stretch reflex Liddell and Sherrington (Chapter 3) had actually advanced beyond the strict concept of reflex action when they realized that the excitability of the acting motoneurones is continuously modified by the autogenetic information arriving from the length-meters and tension-meters residing in the working muscles.

In the stretch reflex, as studied in the extensors of the decerebrate cat, the following chain of events was known to Sherrington: (i) extension produces impulses in muscular end-organs; (ii) these run to the motoneurones of their own muscle and there set up excitation which (iii) counteracts lengthening because it implies shortening of the muscle. The 'reflex', as a concept, would have only required the afferent impulses to elicit certain efferent impulse patterns. In the present case re-evoked sensory information is returned across the centre to the acting motoneurones in order to adjust output so as to correct for the effect of stretch. The idea of a 'negative feedback' is implicit in this reasoning and, when Sherrington spoke of antigravity muscles and assumed the stretch reflex to be a basic component in standing, he visualized the chain of events as an operative mechanism or 'item of behaviour' in its own right. The experiments to be described have added new facts and ideas which have opened the road to a better understanding of problems of co-ordination. I have referred to them here and elsewhere under the general heading of 'motor control'.

In the correspondence with Alexander Forbes (quoted on p. 77), Sherrington had expressed some ideas on the rôle of the muscle receptors in contraction, and in the Linacre Lecture he had been wondering about the significance of the motor fibres running to the muscle spindles. Yet in 1930, when with Eccles he published the much-quoted paper on the contraction value of motoneurones (Chapter 3) and showed that there were two characteristic fibre groups in the ventral roots (Plate 12), he must have believed that practically all these fibres innervated muscle fibres of the ordinary type because total isometric tension for the muscle was divided by total number of fibres, in order to obtain average tension values for individual moto-neurones in different muscles. In 1945 Lars Leksell in Stock-holm took up this problem for systematic analysis and found that the small fibres did not set up any measurable tension to ventral root stimulation after the large ones had been eliminated by pressure block. Instead, selective stimulation of the small fibres produced a discharge of sensory impulses in the dorsal roots, provided that the muscle was slightly extended. Since only the spindles among muscle end-organs receive an efferent innervation it was clear that their muscle fibres had been stimulated.

For further discussion of all these problems it is now neces-sary to introduce some terms commonly used in this field. The 'ordinary' muscle fibres with which we have been dealing exclus-ively hitherto are called *extrafusal*, those of the spindles *intra-fusal* fibres, two terms introduced by Sherrington. The large and fast nerve fibres destined for extrafusal muscles fall into the *alpha* category of Erlanger and Gasser's scheme relating con-duction velocities to fibre size (80–115 metres per second), the small ones were found by Leksell to have average conduction velocities 20–38 per cent of the alphas and so they fitted into the category of *gamma fibres*. Hunt has since introduced the term *fusimotor* nerve fibres for them. A few spindles are in addition innervated by a branch from the alpha fibres.

A first schematic presentation of the anatomical situation is given in Fig. 29. The muscle spindle is placed in parallel with the main muscle in this diagram and the tendon organ is left out so

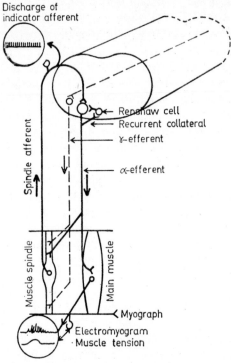

Fig. 29 Diagram of extrafusal and intrafusal innervation of muscle and the circuits involved. The muscle spindle with its large primary afferent, placed in parallel with the main muscle sends its message monosynaptically to the motoneurone in the spinal cord. The ventral horn cell is provided with a recurrent collateral through the Renshaw cell. The gamma motor nerves (broken line) go to the muscular poles of the spindle which they contract, thereby exerting a pull on the sense organ. The supraspinal control of the gamma motoneurones is indicated (within the spinal cord). For analysis, this circuit can be intercepted at several points but the diagram only shows a recording from a branch of the dorsal root as well as a myogram and electromyogram, all results displayed on cathode ray oscillographs.

as not to complicate the issue too much at this stage. The 'in parallel' location of the muscle spindle was functionally demonstrated in single fibre experiments by Sir Bryan Matthews who in 1933 published an extensive electrophysiological study of the muscular sense organs. This paper has remained a fundamental source of information ever since. The 'in parallel' arrangement means that the spindle will respond to stretch but becomes silent in extrafusal contraction because it will then be unloaded, unless co-contraction of the intrafusal fibres takes place. These facts are illustrated in the schematic diagram of Fig. 30, which also shows (Matthews, 1933) that the Golgi tendon organ operates as a pure tension recorder and thus mostly responds to a sufficiently hard pull on the tendon. It has a considerably higher threshold than the muscle spindle and so its normal stimulus is likely to be muscle contraction.

In the diagram of Fig. 29 it is also seen that the impulses from

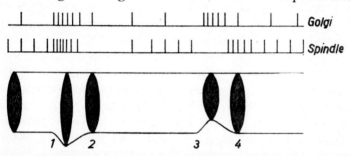

Fig. 30 Diagram illustrating the response of a Golgi tendon organ and a spindle ending during stretch and contraction of the muscle. The muscle is drawn below in black, between lines indicating its insertions. (Granit, *Receptors and Sensory Perception*, Yale University Press. New Haven, 1955)

the muscle spindle reach the spinal cord by the monosynaptic route and excite the motoneurones of their own muscle. This is the autogenetic alpha circuit of the stretch reflex, briefly analysed in Chapters 3 and 5. The scheme makes the spindle afferents wholly monosynaptic but this is an over-simplification.

On the output side we recognize in the diagram the recurrent collaterals with their Renshaw cells which form the local feed-back mechanism for stabilization of the discharge and for 'motor contrast', described in the previous chapter. We shall return to it below.

Fig. 29 also contains the simplified gamma circuit. The gamma terminals can be seen to innervate the intrafusal muscle fibres of the spindle, located on either side of the *nuclear bag*

(Sherrington's term) around which the spirals of the end-organ, giving rise to the fast fibres, coil themselves. The gamma fibres overlap a great deal on individual spindles, as is also shown functionally (Hunt and Kuffler, 1951). Since some 30 per cent of the ventral root fibres belong to the gamma group, the system is extremely potent, and full activation of it will stretch the sensory endings and thus cause them to discharge impulses at rates, maximally, as high as 300 impulses per second (Eldred, Granit, and Merton, 1953), in spite of which the tension on the spindles never becomes large enough to be measurable at the tendon of an intact muscle. These impulses are, of course, the ones that elicit the stretch reflex, and thus the gamma loop through the muscle represents an indirect device for activating the muscle to which the spindles belong (together with its synergists).

Fig. 29 finally shows that the gamma neurones in the spinal cord are under central control (Granit and Kaada, 1952). This means that tonic and phasic activity can also be started by commands from above, which, through the loop, influence the state of depolarization of the motoneurones. The existence of supraspinal control makes some sense out of the monosynaptic arrangement because it means that central commands across the gamma loop reach the motoneurones with a minimum of interference. In relation to the moving masses of bones, joints, and muscles, the gain of a millisecond in speed that the monosynaptic connection entails can hardly in itself be very important.

The diagram of Fig. 29 is a simplified presentation of the internal organization of the muscle spindle. It has been assumed to contain only one end-organ, the *primary* ending (using a term of Ruffini's, 1898) with its monosynaptic afferents. There is also another type of spindle ending, the *secondary receptor* to which it will be necessary to return below. Its afferents are of smaller calibre and hence conduct more slowly (Merton, 1953; Hunt, 1954). A good case can be made out for discussing the primary end-organ and general principles of control before considering the secondaries, because so much of our present knowledge is derived from extensor muscles in which excitatory phenomena dominate and these, in all muscles, are caused by the large afferents from the primaries. The Group II muscular afferents were shown by Lloyd to cause inhibition of the extensors and excitation of the flexors and Hunt (1954) found these fibres to derive from spindle secondaries. Another problem concerns the physiological conditions under which the secondaries are operative.

The diagram of Fig. 29 also left out the tendon organs whose circuits are mostly disynaptic (Laporte and Lloyd, 1952) though some of them apparently run through a greater number of synapses (Eccles, Lundberg). Their effect on extensor motoneurones is inhibitory. Sherrington's autogenetic inhibition is dependent upon the amount of tension (Granit, 1950; Granit and Ström, 1952). At the same time tendon organs excite the flexor motoneurones reciprocally. In flexors we also find autogenetic inhibition as a response to tension (Bianconi, Granit, Reis), but there is no concomitant reciprocal excitation of the extensors so that the circuits of the tendon organs in the two antagonists are highly asymmetrical (Granit, 1952). Whatever is done to the flexors (stretch, contraction) seems to inhibit the extensors (cf. Cooper and Creed, 1927). According to the most recent work of Eccles and his colleagues there is also a component of 'presynaptic inhibition' from flexor tendon organ afferents influencing extensor terminals. One may read some biological meaning into this asymmetry of pattern, because extensors are large muscles, supporting the weight of the body, and therefore needing to be inhibited when the smaller flexors are thrown into action.

Thus, what should be remembered about the tendon organs is their general rôle as inhibitory tension-sensitive endings in autogenetic control. It is not intended in what follows to discuss the function of muscle end-organs in connections other than those throwing light on Sherrington's work. It is clear that the projections of tendon organs to interneurones raise a number of interesting problems which reflect the existence of spinal and supraspinal control at that level (Job, Lundberg, Hufschmidt). Thus, for instance, sensitivity to inhibition is increased in the spinal animal relative to the decerebrate one (Job, 1953). Lundberg with his co-workers has taken up the analysis of such problems while Hufschmidt has interested himself in the functional aspects of tension-sensitive inhibition in man.

In order to understand how stimulation of the gamma fibres influences the discharge from the primary end-organ, Fig. 31,

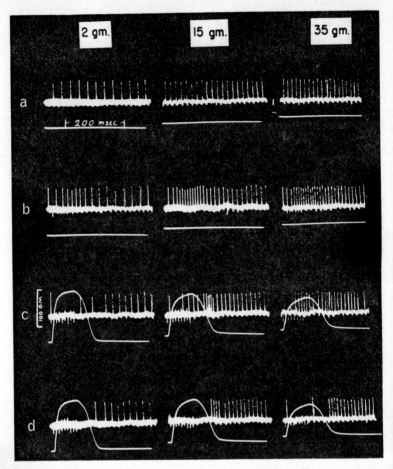

Fig. 31 Effect of contraction on the response to small-nerve gamma stimulation. The recordings are from single *A*- or spindle receptor from flexor *digitorum longus* at initial tensions of 2, 15 and 35 g. The second beam indicates strain gauge response. (a) Baseline discharge. (b) Stimulation of isolated gamma fibre (nine stimuli at 10 msec. intervals at beginning of sweep). Note that the effect on afferent discharge increases as muscle tension is raised. No muscle contraction results. (d) Similar stimulation of a portion of the ventral root containing no gamma fibres; there is cessation of discharge during contraction. (c) Simultaneous stimulation of gamma fibres as in (b) and large alpha fibres as in (d). At 2 g. tension there is a pause in the discharge, while at 15 and 35 g. gamma stimulation becomes increasingly effective. Potentials, 0·2 mV.; maximal tetanus tension, 140 g. (Hunt and Kuffler, *J. Physiol.*, 1951, *113*, 283)

Plate 9   Sherrington, Graham Brown, and Fulton, from a larger photograph, taken by Dr Arnold C. Klebs at his home, *Les Terrasses*. (By courtesy of Miss Madeline Stanton, Yale Historical Library)

Plate 10   J. C. Eccles visiting Sherrington at Ipswich in 1936. (By courtesy of Professor, Sir John Eccles, Canberra)

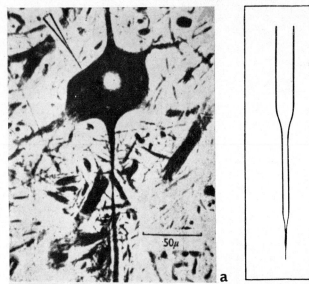

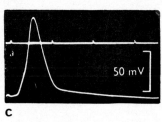

a

b

c

Plate 11 (a) Photomicrograph of cat spinal motoneurone and axon (pyridine silver stain), with a super-imposed tracing of microelectrode tip at the same magnification to indicate the small proportion of total cell sur-face that would be damaged by direct puncture. (b) Scale diagram to show form of the Pyrex microelectrodes used. (c) The spike action potential recorded intracellularly from the motoneurone in response to antidromic electrical stimulus to the first sacral ventral root. Note the reference line for zero membrane potential with time in milliseconds marked thereon and the voltage scale to the right. The spike is preceded by an electrical artifact caused by the shock to the ventral root. (Brock, Coombs and Eccles, *J. Physiol.*, 1952, 177, 431)

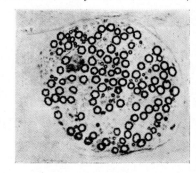

Plate 12 Cross-section of the branch of deafferented motor nerve leading to the lateral gastrocnemius muscle. Note the typical difference between large alpha fibres and small gamma fibres. (Eccles and Sherrington, *Proc. Roy. Soc.*, 1930, *B106*, 326)

from a paper by Hunt and Kuffler (1951), should be consulted. The records are discharges from a single, large spindle afferent, the lower tracing representing muscle tension. There are separate stimulating electrodes on alpha and gamma fibres. The muscle (a cat extensor) is studied at three initial lengths represented by the initial tensions, 2, 15, and 35 grams (vertically). Records (a) (horizontally) show the background or base-line discharges at the three extensions; records (d), the pause during contraction when alpha fibres alone are stimulated. In records (b), a single gamma fibre is stimulated (9 successive shocks) and it is clear that its effect on the spindle is more marked at greater extensions as in Leksell's work. Finally, in (c), both the alpha fibres and the single gamma fibre are stimulated together. As long as the muscle is relatively slack (2 gram tension) the pause is dominant but at greater extensions it is filled out with spikes owing to co-contraction of the stimulated intrafusal fibres. (Within limits, all muscles contract better the more they are extended.)

In experiments shifting the emphasis from the peripheral events and reflex studies to general problems of motor control (Eldred, Granit, and Merton), the gamma innervation of the spindle was proved to hold the key to some of the riddles that Sherrington had left unsolved. It was pointed out above (Chapter 3) that a characteristic feature of decerebrate rigidity is that it disappears after section of the dorsal root carrying the appropriate afferents. Now, since after this operation the ventral roots are still intact, why could not their efferent barrage of impulses, assumed to be released by section of the brain stem, still continue to maintain the limb rigid? Clearly one possible answer might be that the 'release' would largely concern the brain stem gamma mechanisms, because this system had been found to be strongly represented in that region (Granit and Kaada, 1952). Actually, in decerebrate rigidity, there is a strong outflow through the gamma fibres which would keep the intrafusal muscles tonically contracted, biasing the spindles to discharge tonically. On this view 'intrafusal cramps' would be the indirect cause of extrafusal contraction in decerebrate rigidity. The circuit capable of producing this effect is easily traced in the diagram of Fig. 29.

This hypothesis could not be tested by using the exaggerated

11

stretch reflex of a limb extensor directly, because section of the dorsal roots would automatically stop the inflow of spindle impulses and this would merely be a repetition of the old Sherrington experiment. Instead, a Magnus-de Kleijn reflex to turning of the head was used because this also is exaggerated in the decerebrate state. A reflex from a higher level can be

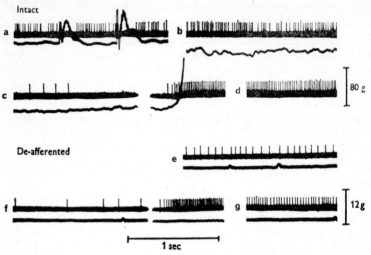

Fig. 32 Reflex activation of alpha and gamma systems by head movement in the vertical plane. Record (a): rigid decerebrate cat with brisk ankle jerk and spontaneous alpha activity, the myograph shows tendon tap succeeded by jerk. Records from soleus spindle with head level (record (b)), flexed backward (c), and suddenly, at the interruption of the traces, flexed downward and held there (d). After deafferentation the same sequence ((e)–(g)) produces gamma response but no alpha discharge. Initial tension approximately 85 g. (Eldred, Granit and Merton, *J. Physiol.*, 1953, *122*, 498)

tested before and after section of the dorsal roots in the lumbar and sacral region.

In record (a) of Fig. 32, in which the upper tracing is from a soleus muscle spindle and the lower one reproduces tension in the soleus muscle, a couple of tendon taps are first given to show ankle jerks together with the pause of the spindles in contraction. (b) shows the base-line at an initial tension of 85 grams. There are continuous small fluctations of tension of the maintained stretch reflex. In (c), the head of the animal has been

firmly grasped and held level for a while. There is some inhibition affecting both the spindles and the muscle. In (d), the head
is turned downwards, which elicits a powerful reflex contraction,
the myograph swinging out of focus, in spite of which the intrafusal fibres are reflexly co-contracted to such a degree that the
spindle discharge actually increases (instead of being silenced)
and reaches a very high maintained value. This effect can only
have been caused by excitation of the efferent spindle fibres.
The experiments so far carried out merely serve as controls.
Then follows deafferentation by dorsal root section. Record (e)
illustrates the new base-line. In (f) and (g) the experiment
carried out in (c) and (d) is repeated with the deafferented
muscle. The spindle is still excited a great deal, in point of fact,
much as before deafferentation (d), but the muscle has remained quiet. Clearly the gamma effect on the spindles has come
through, as if there still were 'gamma release', but after root
section the afferent spindle impulses can no longer reach the
spinal cord to stimulate the alpha motoneurones. The latter
remain silent. The experiment therefore fully supports the hypothesis that the Magnus-de Kleijn reflex was driven by way of the
gamma loop. Careful inspection of record (d) also shows that
spindle activation precedes or coincides with alpha activation.

P. B. C. Matthews and G. Rushworth (1958) then recalled
that Erlanger and Gasser in 1929 had shown that when cocaine
paralyses nerve fibres, the effect is first seen in those of small
diameter. By using suitable concentrations of a cocaine solution
applied in cotton wool on to the nerve, it proved possible for
them to keep the large fibres on both the afferent and the
efferent side functioning while for some time only the gamma
fibres were paralysed. In this way they could use the maintained
stretch reflex of the soleus muscle as their indicator and prove
that it vanished during selective paralysis of the gamma fibres.

Sherrington's decerebrate rigidity is thus largely caused by a
tonic release of the gamma system following section of the brain
stem. This leads to shortening of the intrafusal fibres with consequent firing of the large spindle afferents. By the ensuing
stimulation of their motoneurones the extrafusal muscles are in
their turn forced to contract in an attempt, so to speak, to adjust
their length to intrafusal length. No sooner has this adjustment
taken place than the spindles are unloaded and cease to activate

the motoneurones or do so at a slower rate. The extrafusal fibres can then relax but in doing so they again exert pull on the spindles and the cycle repeats itself. This takes place asynchronously and so the base-line oscillates as in Fig. 32, record (b), the lower tracing illustrating the myogram.

Similarly a thermostat in maintaining a constant temperature keeps oscillating around a mean value because the mercury column of its 'sense organ', the thermometer, makes and breaks a contact putting the supply of heat on and off according to the plus or minus sign of the deviation from the desired temperature. The tonic gamma bias on the spindles make them detectors of deviations of length, and in the life of the organism bias is likely to be optimally adjusted to the needs of the moment in terms of extrafusal load and length. The excessive gamma bias of the decerebrate animal produces a caricature of a normal function, visible as exaggerated standing and 'antigravity' reactions, but it is really a caricature of the function by which a 'wanted length' is maintained, in this case 'unwantedly'. The 'wanted optimum length' for the execution of tonic functions is a concept that carries us far beyond the 'reflex movement', but when we have now seen that spindle activation across the gamma loop really can force the extrafusal muscle to assume a definite length, how can this concept be avoided? It is inherent in the design of the loop. The man-made machine of our analogy is an imitation of principles laid down in the living machines. We have seen that even in the relatively simple loop that has now been discussed, accessory feedback mechanisms are also included in the design. The recurrent collaterals and the Golgi tendon organs which have already been mentioned belong to this category. Quantitative treatment, though highly desirable, is therefore beset with difficulties. The theoretical problems posed by the gamma loop and the stretch reflex as a servo-mechanism have been considered by Merton (1953).

In the normal life of the organism a number of higher centres must be engaged in computing the information setting the gamma bias. We can see something of this in the transition from sleep to wakefulness. Muscle tone is not needed in sleep but is required as soon as the animal wakes up. In lightly anaesthetized animals it is possible to follow fluctuations of wakefulness by studying the discharge from the spindles, preferably in combination with electroencephalography which serves as a second index of variations in the degree of alertness or 'arousal' (Berger, Bremer, Magoun, Moruzzi). In such experiments it has been found that the spindle discharge and the electroencephalogram indicate 'arousal' in parallel (C. von Euler and Söderberg, 1957). The ramifications of this theme cannot be followed up in detail.

Clearly Sherrington was right in thinking of the spindles as length-meters and for good reasons he was worried about the significance of the motor innervation of the intrafusal muscles. The spindle is indeed a kind of sensori-motor instrument and its physiological rôle is bound to remain unintelligible unless considered very broadly in relation to 'motor control'. It may be instructive at this point to recall a statement made in Chapter 2 (p. 26): 'Very often we find that the pioneers who laid the groundwork had so many pieces of the next puzzle at their disposal that it ought to have been an easy matter to insert them and so advance the few steps needed for the next new generalization.' While in the present case advancement of technique made it easier to take the 'few steps needed', the notion that the stretch reflex might be driven strongly indirectly by contractions of the intrafusal fibres so as to maintain 'tone' did not depend on technique. It merely required awareness of the existence of a motor innervation of the spindle and, on such scant knowledge, this idea was, in fact, anticipated by G. Rossi of Florence in 1927, before Sir Bryan Matthews had published his paper on the properties of muscle spindles as sensory instruments. Rossi made no attempt to prove his thesis (published in Italian). Matthews, in some experiments, did stimulate muscle nerves at strengths capable of activating motor fibres of small calibre and noticed that this elicited a spindle discharge, inferring likewise that motor nerves to spindles had been excited. This was twelve years before Leksell published his work. Rossi's paper was unearthed by Eldred, Granit, and Merton (1953) when they had finished the experiments reviewed above.

In assigning a definite rôle to the gamma system in decerebrate rigidity and in the maintenance of tone, one should not forget that the average level of depolarization of any particular pool of motoneurones is influenced by many factors. The ventral horn cells are individual centres of convergence, as Sherrington always emphasized, and if other circuits projecting on to them keep silent, it is not likely that the gamma loop alone would be able to activate them tonically. Some support from elsewhere would generally be required. Information on such factors has been supplied by Moruzzi and Pompeiano and will be found in the book by Dow and Moruzzi (*Physiology and Pathology of the Cerebellum*, 1958).

These problems are well exemplified by types of rigidity which, as Sherrington (p. 94) had pointed out, could not be identical with the decerebrate form. One is cerebellar rigidity, which was studied by L. J. Pollock and L. Davis (1931) who found that it persisted after dorsal root section. In their experiments the cerebellum was made anaemic together with the brain in front of it by tying up the supplying blood vessels. The section through the brain stem of the Sherrington preparation would be in front of the 'section by anaemia'. The rigidity that ensues is strong and also characterized by opisthotonus, which is a contraction of the neck muscles turning the head upwards. In this form of rigidity the spindles of the contracting extensor muscles behave as if they were dissociated from active participation (Granit, Holmgren, and Merton, 1954). They respond passively, being silenced in contraction, as, of course, would be the case if the peripheral spindle apparatus were left to its own devices. The picture is totally different from the one illustrated in Fig. 32. In agreement with these findings it could also be shown that removal of gamma control by cocainization of the nerve had no influence whatsoever on cerebellar rigidities (P. B. C. Matthews). This form is therefore an *alpha rigidity* while Sherrington's decerebrate preparation is more of a *gamma rigidity*.

In the end, Sherrington came to the final conclusion—generally accepted in his lifetime—that tone was a postural reflex, a view that arose from his work on decerebrate rigidity and the finding that this state of 'exaggerated tone' disappeared after dorsal root section and hence originated in a sense organ. At the International Neurological Congress in Berne, 1931, where he presided over a meeting on this subject, he nevertheless could not suppress some anxiety about the flexors having been neglected in the study of postural reflexes. Would they have a 'lengthening reaction', he asked, among other things. 'The term tonus,' he said, speaking of its origin, 'comes to us from a time when the doctrine of its existence or non-existence was almost an article of faith. Then, later, for many years, it stood for a general condition of slight tension rather mysteriously obtaining in all healthy muscles at all times, a somewhat elusive property; how far peripheral or central, and whether reflex or not, was answered differently by different observers.' Today, while one would still be willing to give the postural reflex a rôle to play in tone, it seems impossible to identify the two concepts. It can hardly be termed a 'postural reflex' when the wakening animal activates its gamma motoneurones and probably at the same time throws into operation some internuncial cells with direct projections on alpha motoneurones. But tone can still be called a 'somewhat elusive property' and one may even raise the question of 'how far peripheral or central'. In tone we postulate an element of 'maintenance' of some slight state of contraction for which a tonic discharge is required, on occasion perhaps merely a high subliminal level of depolarization in certain motoneurones so that they are prepared to fire on very slight provocation. In tone many functions, nervous as well as muscular, are organized for co-operation and the best we can do is to study them one by one as well as when they are acting in co-ordination. As we shall see and have seen partly already, the problem of tone involves *circuit analysis* rather than the study of reflexes alone.

Sherrington originally (in *Integrative Action*) thought that there were two separable systems of motor innervation, one phasic the other tonic; but the impression left from a study of his papers is that the latter eventually came to be identified with extensor muscles counteracting gravity while the phasic system chiefly comprised the flexors. Gradually he ceased to emphasize the differentiation as originally formulated. In Sherrington's laboratory, Denny-Brown added fresh aspects to this problem when he found that the slowly contracting, deep-lying muscles, which in the laboratory animals tend to be red in colour, such as the soleus and the crureus, were the ones that responded most easily by stretch reflexes. Soleus, for instance, is synergistic with the gastrocnemius which lies above it and is a 'white' muscle.

The method of functional isolation of single fibres in the ventral roots suggested a way of attacking the problem of whether there really are preferentially tonic motoneurones. To this end it is necessary to force a neurone to maximum performance. Otherwise one may be dealing merely with different grades of activity. Post-activation potentiation by a high-frequency tetanus of the afferent muscle nerve (ventral roots being cut and filaments of it placed on recording electrodes) suggested itself as the method *par preference*. When this experiment was tried with extensors (Granit, Henatsch, and Steg, 1956) it soon turned out that (i) only a limited number of motoneurones could be forced to discharge repetitively to stretch following such activation and that (ii) these were motoneurones represented in the lower range of the calibre spectrum, i.e. those conducting at relatively slow alpha rates. These motoneurones easily became, as it were, spastic or hyper-responsive to stretch. The rapidly conducting alpha motoneurones refused to give more than a burst of impulses to maintained stretch. Thus with respect to the muscular afferents some motoneurones really are tonic, others predominantly phasic.

By these experiments Eccles and Lundberg (1958) were induced to apply the intracellular technique to a study of the duration of after-hyperpolarization as a function of axonal conduction velocity. They found that the slower the conduction velocity, the longer the duration of after-hyperpolarization. Thus the tonic motoneurones, prone to respond by maintained repetitive firing at slow rates in response to stretch, were also the ones in which long-lasting after-hyperpolarization would promote firing at such rates. It was pointed out in Chapter 5 that tonic firing of motoneurones is actually characterized by very slow rates of discharge (Denny-Brown, Adrian, and Bronk).

All those results mean that tonic motoneurones would be well represented in the soleus, because its fibre spectrum, on an average, is known to comprise a greater number of small fibres than that of the gastrocnemius. Eccles and Lundberg also found that the soleus had especially dense projections from the monosynaptic spindle afferents. For all these reasons the soleus muscle has lately become something of a favourite in studies of tonic reflexes and motor control. Much of what one finds to be characteristic for tonic motoneurones, studied individually, recurs as a statistical property in the average response of the soleus. Thus, for instance, when it was shown that antidromic or recurrent inhibition was particularly potent on tonic motoneurones (Granit, Pascoe, and Steg, 1957), it was soon found that the same effect could be reproduced with the soleus in experiments comparing it with the gastrocnemius (Kuno, 1959, Eccles, Iggo, and Ito, 1960).

With the tonic motoneurones we are now facing an assembly of 'overlapping' properties all of which seem to contribute to the same well co-ordinated end result: these motoneurones are very much dependent on the gamma loop; they make use of slowly contracting muscles requiring slow rates of discharge; in tonic firing the adapted slope constants of the curves relating impulse

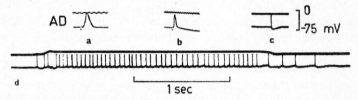

Fig. 33 Intracellular recording from soleus motoneurone showing the response to stretch of soleus. (a)–(c) Response of the motoneurone to a single antidromic (*AD*) shock to its motor nerve, taken at different speeds of recording. Time in msec. in (a) and (b). Note after-hyperpolarization (c) and response to stretch, (d), recorded by upper horizontal line. The spike of the motoneurone is of the order of 73 mV. (Granit, Phillips, Skoglund, and Steg, *J. Neurophysiol.*, 1957, *20*, 470)

frequency to membrane current are small, as explained in the previous chapter; the motoneurones have long-lasting after-hyperpolarizations and are strongly influenced by recurrent inhibition. Fig. 33 shows a soleus motoneurone firing in response to stretch in a decerebrate animal. The record is intracellular.

Why is recurrent inhibition strong on tonic motoneurones? Questions of this kind can only be answered by placing any particular function into a co-ordinated totality, as we have done, and, then studying the mechanisms in action. 'Why' is generally held to be an unscientific question, but if we regard living machinery as pieces of engineering like man-made machinery, then, in this particular case, a number of sensible reasons can be given for adding 'stabilization' and 'motor contrast' to a maintenance function of the kind studied, even when it may seem superfluous in view of what the membrane itself can achieve by adaptation and after-hyperpolarization.

It is possible to suggest other answers. And they may all contain an element of truth. Most mechanisms in the nervous system have various tasks to perform and we can but humbly admit our ignorance when trying to make sense out of the masterpieces of biological engineering involved in motor control. It is hard enough to unravel some major features of design. For instance, one might imagine that the phasic motoneurones suppress the tonic ones by recurrent inhibition because Holmgren and Merton (1953) found that antidromic shocks, exciting 25 per cent of the fibres and hence stimulating large ones selectively, sufficed to give very strong recurrent inhibition. Granit, Pascoe, and Steg, who suggested this possibility, were unwilling to subscribe to this explanation because they found little other evidence for it. But the Canberra group has taken it up a second time and now, on re-reading *Integrative Action*, I find Sherrington stating 'the very muscles that to the observer are most obviously under excitation by the *tonic* system are those most obviously inhibited by the *phasic* reflex system'. His examples, as stated, concern extensors (tonic) being reciprocally inhibited by flexors (phasic), but it has actually been found by V. Wilson and his co-workers that, while recurrent inhibition is very potent on extensors, it tends to be weak on flexors. These display more of the facilitation that Renshaw had also seen in some cases. The arrangement is reminiscent of the asymmetry observed with the reflexes from the tendon organs (p. 147). We cannot deny that one task of recurrent inhibition might be to make all phasic movements, be they started from flexors or extensors, suppress tonic discharges which are always likely to be more prominent in extensors. The Canberra group has not found any organizational feature in recurrent inhibtion other than proximity in the spinal cord.

The problems concerning recurrent inhibition, merely scanned in this presentation, may seem very special to the reader but this is not so. Cajal found recurrent fibres in nearly all nerve centres that he studied and regarded them as an essential feature of nervous organization. These circuits have made possible very precise formulations of problems of feedback in terms of impulse frequency, as pointed out in the last chapter, and their study has for the first time opened up a road towards quantitative analysis of problems of co-ordination, or as Sherrington would have said, 'integration'.

The safeguarding of one particular purpose, such as slow rates of discharge in tonic motoneurones, by a number of overlapping mechanisms is an expression of the principle of 'safety in numbers' of which many other examples from the central nervous system could be given. Let us apply it here in an attempt to understand 'afterdischarge' which Sherrington held to be so characteristic for reflex action (cf. Chapter 3). Clearly inter-neurones must go on firing for a while after cessation of external stimulation and provide the necessary support for depolarization of motoneurones. Interneurones tend to fire high-frequency bursts instead of single impulses at slow rates (cf. the Renshaw cells). This may be a property of the chemical mechanism (Eccles); and high slope constants of the curves relating firing rate to depolarization may be another factor since this means high amplification (Chapter 6). The very large number of interneurones will strengthen the probability of interaction, and reverberating chains (Ranson, Lorente de Nó), being an internuncial feature of design, will continue to stir up activity for some time after cessation of external stimulation. The dendrites of the motoneurones on to which two-thirds of the synapses project are likely to maintain a subliminal state of depolarization after the discharge of a soma spike and for this reason could serve as 'reservoirs' in the way the soma in some invertebrate neurones maintains a state of depolarization while the firing of full-size spikes is restricted to the axon hillock (Bullock and Hagiwara). Finally, postactivation potentiation will be favoured by the high rates of internuncial firing. All these factors may contribute to 'afterdischarge'.

In studying the various components of the circuit, illustrated in Fig. 29, the muscle has so far been neglected. Yet this is the organ that in the end is to be controlled and so the muscle must be supposed to derive the benefit of all the features of design which have been described. Somehow they must find their expression in performance. In a way alpha control is a simpler proposition because it is likely to produce power and speed of action in the muscle combinations available to the brain, both automatic and volitional, whereas the properties which muscles acquire by the gamma loop and its length-detector, the spindle, must be related to the fundamental fact that muscle is a machine engaged in translating (length) extension into tension. This it does along curves which are approximately linear as long as output frequency is constant, as it is, for instance, in tone. As an example, let us consider the sensitivity of muscle to changes of extension. For a constant alpha output the slope of the curve relating tension to extension depends upon the number of alpha motoneurones engaged in the act. Steep slopes require the firing of a large number of motoneurones. This means that small changes of length cannot be accurately translated into changes of tension unless a large number of alpha motoneurones have been mobilized. Again, by varying gamma bias a constant sensitivity to changes of extension can be retained at any given extension because any alteration of extension could easily be compensated for by a reduction or increase of bias (P. B. C. Matthews, 1959).

If a muscle were given the task of carrying the same load at different extensions, a reasonably good method, considered from the point of view of bio-engineering, would certainly be for the organism to make use of its length-measuring device and always put in the compensatory amount of gamma bias. This reasoning assumes that variations of discharge frequency are small in static performance. Control by a variation of frequency would be especially useful in phasic action and for movements requiring exercise of strength. We have seen in the previous chapter that static performance of motoneurones takes place at a steady 'adapted' rate of discharge.

These considerations are meant to serve as an introduction to a reconsideration of Sherrington's 'lengthening' and 'shortening reactions', presented in Chapter 3. These were said to endow the muscle with 'plastic' properties such as those characterizing smooth muscle. Sherrington's two 'reactions' actually imply solving the problem stated in the previous paragraph. A constant tension must be held at different lengths. While I can be said to have pointed out one way in which this could be done sensibly by the organism, clearly I have failed to show how the decerebrate animal would understand how to apply the suggested method. It is asking a great deal from it. But before taking up this problem, let us first exclude the possibility that 'plastic' behaviour could occur in the absence of sensory information from the muscle. In our laboratory deafferented animals with alpha rigidity have been studied and in them tension is a linear function of extension and the curve is very steep (Pompeiano, 1960). Any change of length must immediately be reflected in a change of tension. Long ago Sherrington also noted that in very strong rigidities that are likely to contain an alpha component (as we understand it today), plastic reactions were absent, and Pollock and Davis made the same observation in their animals with cerebellar alpha rigidities which, as we have seen, are lacking gamma control. It seems clear and today it is almost self-evident that the muscle-machine of the decerebrate animal cannot maintain the same tension at different lengths in the absence of sensory information.

Another observation of Sherrington's carries us farther. He found that an injection of strychnine abolished plastic behaviour and strychnine antagonizes postsynaptic inhibitions (Bradley and Eccles, 1953). It is evident that if an increase of extension could command a mechanism of length-sensitive inhibition, this would be a way for the organism to reduce *automatically* the number of active motoneurones in compensation for an increase of length. For this task the tendon organs are too simply designed because they have a high threshold and would either cease to fire as soon as the constant tension had been achieved or else at this tension would always fire at the same slow rate. In the extension of the lengthening reaction they would, of course, have to be able to produce graded inhibition in order to antagonize the excitatory spindle afferents which fire in direct proportion to length, recruiting fresh motoneurones in the manner we have described (for the stretch reflex). We have therefore to postulate the existence of length-sensitive inhibition if we ascribe the lengthening reaction to inhibitory removal of alpha motoneurones. In extensors the spindle secondaries possess this very property. They could automatically produce inhibition in proportion to extension and relieve the decerebrate animal of the difficulty of having to understand how to adjust bias for the primaries, so as to compensate for the increase in extension.

These considerations should not be regarded as the final word in the matter of Sherrington's lengthening and shortening reactions but rather as specimens of how one would have to reason on the basis of available knowledge. The old experiments were carried out with fully innervated limbs and so reciprocal adjustments would also have to be taken into account. Experiments with isolated muscles can only separate ingredients for the understanding of plastic action. The full story must be developed in collaboration with clinical neurology which deals with complex disturbances of plasticity, rigidity, and spasticity.

The pathology of motor control goes far beyond anything that can be forced into the framework of reflexology. Since clinical work so far has been hampered by lack of methods for attacking the indirect spindle route, it has encountered great difficulties in trying to understand problems of control. Clinical science tends to throw the emphasis on the 'central' (motor cortex, basal ganglia) disturbances for which some evidence can be obtained by pathological anatomy, but it is clear that whatever the 'central disturbance', it must take effect through the spinal, sensori-motor and muscular mechanisms that we have been discussing. In the end, understanding of the principles which physiology is now beginning to unravel must also become useful in clinical work.

At the moment the easiest to understand is the clasp-knife reaction. This is observed when the limb of the decerebrate animal (or of some patients) is over-extended. The spindle secondaries will go on trying to compensate by inhibition for the excitation which the primaries produce when the muscle is extended, but this compensation is incomplete and so tension rises in spite of it. At a certain tension, then, the tendon organs add their effect to the inhibitory side and the limb goes 'clasp-knife' slack. The tendon organs may even succeed in reflexly inhibiting the gamma fibres so as to remove the excitatory component altogether. There is some evidence for that, as yet not quite conclusive.

We have now placed the spindle secondaries on the stage and so this chapter should be finished by a brief glance at recent work in which their properties have been much in the limelight. Some of the new anatomical disclosures concerning spindle organization require mentioning. The picture which Sybil Cooper, David Barker with his co-workers, and Ian Boyd have drawn of the spindle end-organs has stimulated fresh physiological research and may also be said to have emphasized the truth of a remark of Ruffini's (1898) to the effect that 'apart from the organs of special sense (eye, ear, etc.) the body possesses no terminal organ that can compare with these in richness of nerve-fibres and of nerve endings'.

On returning to the diagram of Fig. 29 dealing with the circuit for the primaries we can see how it should be modified in order to be valid for the secondary endings. On the central side we have to replace the monosynaptic arc by a wholly poly-synaptic circuit. This means that the sensitivity of the spinal cord to impulses from the secondaries is likely to undergo con-siderable fluctuations depending upon how the internuncial cells are balanced. In the periphery the secondaries are 'in parallel' just as the primaries, being situated within the spindle. Within the spindle there are also two kinds of intrafusal muscle fibres, long ones within which lie the nuclear bags of the primaries, called nuclear bag fibres, and short ones with nuclei in chains, and for this reason called nuclear chain fibres. The majority of secondaries derive from these fibres. The primaries possess terminals to both nuclear bags and to nuclear chain fibres. The nuclear chain fibres are also controlled by gamma fibres.

There is a fundamental difference between primaries and secondaries in that only the former have high phasic sensitivity. Sybil Cooper, confirmed by later workers, first showed that the secondaries respond to extension by setting up steady rates of discharge and do not register rate of change of length as do the primaries, by a burst at onset of extension and a pause as soon as relaxation occurs. The secondaries behave as if they had inertia and momentum. Jansen and P. B. C. Matthews have clear evi-dence for separate gamma control of the phasic and tonic response of the primaries and it may well be that this is a con-sequence of the dichotomy of their terminals, nuclear bag termi-nals being responsible for the phasic properties and nuclear chain terminals for the tonic ones. With these few comments we have to leave spindle physiology in the making. They serve to indicate the expanding border of knowledge. The only con-nection which at the moment can be traced between Sherrington's work and the possible rôle of the spindle secondaries has already been mentioned. While the fact that the primaries record velocity of movement, which the secondaries cannot do, is of great importance for all problems of motor control, it is not a fact that can yet be made to throw much light on Sherrington's world of ideas. He had finished his experimental life long before the properties of muscular sense organs and their centrifugal control began to influence physiology. My purpose in introducing the new facts and ideas has merely been to throw light on Sherrington's great work on tone and the stretch reflexes, not to write a review of the field as it stands today, loaded with fresh problems coming from physiology, histology, and servo-theory; for instance, gamma control and spindle activation are known to play an important rôle in the respiratory movements of the intercostal muscles in the chest (C. von Euler, Sears).

Plate 13 Physiology Finals at Oxford during the First World War in 1916. *Upper semicircle:* Woods (N. Zealand), Cluver (S. Africa), Professor Sherrington, Professor Sir F. Gowland Hopkins (Cambridge), Professor Davison, Mr Cox (Sherrington's technician), Johnson (S. Africa). *Middle row:* Penfield, Miss Collier, Emile Holman, Miss Peacy. *Below:* Scott, Witbur, Davison.

England is only represented by two girls. Penfield had been blown up on the S.S. *Sussex* in March of that year and was back after a broken leg. Professor Davison became the founder of Duke University Medical School. (By courtesy of Professor Wilder Penfield, Montreal, who is also responsible for this information)

Plate 14 The last portrait: in his 93rd year. A photograph taken in
March 1950 by Allan Chappelow, M.A., F.R.S.A.

Chapter 8

Literary Works

It is merely a guess on my part when I assume that Lord Gifford was induced to found the Edinburgh Lectures on Natural Religion by his great countryman, David Hume's *Dialogues concerning Natural Religion*. Sherrington, interpreting the founder's intentions, quoted Lord Bacon's famous definition: that 'spark of knowledge of God which may be had by the light of nature and the consideration of created things: and thus can be fairly held to be divine in respect of its object and natural in respect of its source of information'. From these lectures Revealed Religion was banned. The founder's wish was that the subject should be treated as if it were astronomy or chemistry. Sherrington responded to this commission much as did the great painters of the Renaissance to the orders of their patrons. The formal limitations of the theme, so far from checking the flow of inspiration, became a challenge for him to muster all his resources of knowledge and intuition in order to express his ideas on spiritual values, life, and the image of the world as created by modern biological science.

Sherrington with his poetic instinct was never far from a pantheistic identification of himself with Nature. In a lecture on Goethe (1942) he had written congenially: 'A cry of content to be one with Nature! That thought is comfortable to him—more than comfortable, it is welcome. The thought that whether alive or lifeless he is inescapably and for ever a part of Nature—one with her. This, it would seem, is what sustains him. He draws from it his salve for existence, his balsam wherewith he would heal death itself.' While Sherrington saw but little to admire in Goethe's scientific contributions, he identified himself

12

with the 'Nature-intoxicated' poet (his expression) who wrote the unforgettable lines:

> Ihr glücklichen Augen
> Was je ihr gesehn,
> Es sei wie es wolle,
> Es war doch so schön.

Faust, II

Man on his Nature is a work by a scientist who became 'Nature-intoxicated' in a new dimension. His inspiration is the image of the world that modern science is creating, and he believes we can understand Nature in terms which are satisfying to ourselves quite apart from whatever restrictions epistemology may impose upon our modes of thinking. This leads him on to a natural religion of values based on science. By comparison a philosopher of Bertrand Russell's format finds science useful and also pleasing as an intellectual exercise, but when the values to which we revert for our spiritual comfort are concerned he is stirred to an emotional pitch of a far higher order by the aesthetic sensations accepted by all and sundry: 'When I come to die I shall not feel that I have lived in vain. I have seen the earth turn red at evening, the dew sparkling in the morning, and the snow shining under a frosty sun. I have smelt rain after drought, and have heard the strong Atlantic beat upon the granite shores of Cornwall. Science may bestow these and other joys upon more people than could otherwise enjoy them. If so, its power will be wisely used. But when it takes out of life the moments to which life owes it value, science will not deserve admiration, however cleverly and however elaborately it may lead man along the road to despair. The sphere of values lies outside science, except in so far as science consists in the pursuit of knowledge' (Russell: *The Scientific Outlook*).

The sense of wonder, so fundamental with Sherrington, is the key to his poetic transcription of biological facts. Whenever he is deeply engaged by his theme, he is also carried away by a sense of wonder. This makes him take up his brush and start painting. On his palette he mixes naked facts, experimental results, poignant questions, and starts filling his canvas with scenes from the frontiers of biological knowledge. The task excites him. Those sections of *Man on his Nature* are written with abandon, at times almost feverishly. The words come tumbling over each other. Sentences are split into pointed statements. Vivid imagery splashes colour across the pages; thus, for instance:

The eye-ball is a little camera. Its smallness is part of its perfection. A spheroid camera. There are not many anatomical organs where exact shape counts for so much as with the eye. Light which will enter the eye will traverse a lens placed in the right position there. *Will* traverse; all this making of the eye which will see in the light is carried out in the dark. It is a preparing in darkness for use in light. The lens required is biconvex and to be shaped truly enough to focus its pencil of light at the particular distance of the sheet of photosensitive cells at the back, the retina. . . . The light-sensitive screen at the back is the key-structure. It registers a continually changing picture. It receives, takes, and records a moving picture life-long without change of 'plate', through every waking day. It signals its shifting exposures to the brain. . . . And the whole structure with its prescience and all its efficiency, is produced by and out of specks of granular slime arranging themselves as of their own accord in sheets and layers, and acting seemingly on an agreed plan. . . .

. . . The little hollow bladder of the embryo-brain, narrowing itself at two points so as to be triple, thrusts from its foremost chamber to either side a hollow bud. This bud pushes towards the overlying skin. That skin, as though it knew and sympathized, then dips down forming a cuplike hollow to meet the hollow brain stalk growing outward. They meet. The round end of the hollow brain-bud dimples inward and becomes a cup. Concurrently, the ingrowth from the skin nips itself free from its original skin. It rounds itself into a hollow ball, lying in the mouth of the brain-cup. Of this stalked cup, the optic cup, the stalk becomes in a few weeks a cable of a million nerve-fibres connecting the nerve cells within the eyeball itself with the brain. . . . The human eye has about 137 million separate 'seeing' elements spread out in the sheet of the retina. The number of nerve-lines leading from them to the brain gradually condenses down to little over a million. Each of these has in the brain we must think to find its right nerve-exchanges. . . .

. . . As wonders, these things have grown stale through familiarity. The making of this eye out of self-actuated specks, which draw together and multiply and move as if obsessed with one desire, namely, to make the eye-ball. In a few weeks they have done so. Then, their madness over, they sit down and rest satisfied to be life-long what they have made themselves and, so to say, wait for death. . . .

. . . But the chief wonder of all we have not touched on yet.
Wonder of wonders, though familiar even to boredom. So much with
us that we forget it all our time. The eye sends, as we saw, into a cell-
and-fibre forest of the brain throughout the waking day continual
rhythmic streams of tiny, individually evanescent, electrical potentials.
This throbbing streaming crowd of electrified shifting points in the
spongework of the brain bears no obvious semblance in space-pattern,
and even in temporal relation resembles but a little remotely the tiny
two-dimensional upside-down picture of the outside world which the
eye-ball paints on the beginnings of its nerve-fibres to the brain. But
that little picture sets up an electrical storm. And that electrical storm
so set up is one which affects a whole population of brain-cells. . . .

Such 'Nature-intoxicated' and, at times, dramatic scenes
abound in the descriptive sections of *Man on his Nature*. They
are written by an octogenarian and, possibly, age coupled to
vitality has been a real advantage because during his life
Sherrington had seen scientific knowledge expand to become
the powerful structure the young now may take for granted.
He had participated in the process of expansion and knew it
from the inside, not only as a bystander. Age must have been a
special privilege when, as in the example chosen, the leading
facts were based on optical magnification, the great era of
histology, which Sherrington had seen rise to its climax at the
turn of the century. In his youth the microscope was still the
leading invention in the world of biological science and it had
guided his own thinking when he forced a way through to
functional analysis. The light it had thrown on genetic evolution
was to him a living experience and not one become stale through
familiarity. To Sherrington in his old age it must have been
sheer pleasure to lean back for a last sweeping glance over the
full panorama of biological science and tell the young what had
happened. What indomitable strength of mind—at his age! His
almost boyish delight is catching. It echoes a vitality reminiscent
of the works of the eighteenth-century naturalists. It is Linnaean
in its enthusiasm, in its colourful language, Linnaean also in its
background of dormant religiosity (though there is nothing left
of the vindictive God of the Old Testament whom Linnaeus
revered as an Alter ego to the inspired Artificer, gracious,
benevolent and deeply concerned about beauty, order and fitness
in the biological world).

For all that, Sherrington may not have been in the least familiar with the writings of the great botanist. Actually he wove into the general pattern of his book reflections on Jean Fernel (1485–1557), a sixteenth-century physician and savant, to whom he also devoted a separate study (*The Endeavour of Jean Fernel*, 1946). This took him to the Paris of the French Renaissance at the time of Francis I. In England Henry VIII was on the throne, in Germany Charles V. When Henri II succeeded to the throne in France (1547), the Protestant movement in Germany under Luther and Melanchton was well under way. Charles V abdicated in 1555; when Fernel died in 1557 he was physician to Henri II. Fernel had been educated at Ignatius Loyola's college, St Barbe, in the *Quartier Latin*.

The *Endeavour of Jean Fernel* is a scholarly book for specialists in the history of medicine, erudite and critical. It displayed detailed knowledge about the Latin Quarter of the years 1500–50. Once at a dinner party in Paris, sitting next to the late Professor Louis Lapicque of the Sorbonne, I took the liberty of asking him how accurate it was. 'I am the right person to answer this question,' he replied, 'because I live in the house where Jean Fernel lived [or was it a neighbouring house?] and have always been very interested in the history of the *Quartier Latin*. And I would like to testify that Sherrington's knowledge of this region and time is if anything better than my own.' Of Lapicque's knowledge of the history of his university I had been informed in advance by my host, Professor A. Monnier of the Sorbonne.

What concerns us here is simply the place of Jean Fernel in Sherrington's personal sphere of interests. What did he see in the man who created the words 'physiology' and 'pathology' and who wrote the first textbook of physiology (1542) some hundred years before Harvey made physiology an experimental science and Descartes defined the reflex? The work was an outlet, partly at least, for his love of Paris and the French language, both shared with his wife. Though so much of Sherrington's Continental education had been in the German language and in his youth German science dominated the scene, he deeply admired French civilization and, when he had to spend all his days in a chair in the nursing home at Eastbourne, he still enjoyed reading French novels. On his ninetieth birthday

12a

he started an animated discussion with me on *Madame Bovary* which he had recently re-read.

Sherrington's interest in Jean Fernel would have been greatly stimulated by the fact that this man wrote a book akin to *Man on his Nature*—in Latin dialogue to be sure, but at Ipswich school Sherrington, as an exercise, had turned Keats' 'Sonnets on Visiting the Tomb of Burns' into Latin elegiacs. With Fernel he shared a common interest and found in the dialogue *De Abditis Rerum* a statement of his own problems of mind and matter. The author had had the strength to shake himself free from astrology and supernatural causes of disease and reached a view of physiology (in which Fernel included body and soul), that with all its deficiencies was independent and also penetrating enough to make Fernel's book one that was read by intellectuals for a hundred years—until the experimental era began.

Fernel, like Sherrington, belonged to the few who grow more modern with age, and four years before his death he declared that the 'whole book of healing was nothing other than a copy of the code of inviolable laws observable in Nature'. What is Man, he asked in the *Dialogue*, and what is Nature? Briefly put, his reply was that Nature is God's principle working upon matter but Man has powers beyond those of matter, something celestial emerging as 'form' which the Creator sends forth 'as by the breathing of a breath'; not form in the Aristotelian sense but something spiritual, assumed to enter the embryo on the fortieth day after conception!

Another motive for introducing Jean Fernel into *Man on his Nature* was to provide contrast with our times. 'We have to look for a time and scene sufficiently akin to our own for us to share the viewpoints, and then to lay the science along with its religious implications conformably beside our own. Fernel's acceptance of man as within Nature is of significance to us here,' Sherrington said. On asking, why, the reply would seem to be that Fernel felt so urgently that 'Natural Religion and his religion of faith must harmonize'. Across time and space Sherrington felt a bond of sympathy with his aim and the urge behind it.

It is not out of place to consider whether Sherrington acted wisely in providing contrast by introducing Jean Fernel into

Man on his Nature. This complicated the design of the book, and
the reader, with less background than the author, may sometimes feel the strain of focusing and re-focusing across a gap of
four hundred years, a long distance for contrast. To counter-
balance this criticism it should be admitted that his musings on
Jean Fernel really add a specific flavour to the book, truly
Sherringtonian in its intricate artistry. This partly derives from
the ever-present mind-matter problem, partly from the opportunity Sherrington thus had of taking his readers back to the
embryonic stage of biology before letting them witness parturi-
tion and the roaring crescendo of growth in the present time.
'Ah, you know,' Sherrington would have replied to my criticism,
'every one is an artist in his own right' (this being an actual
remark of his).

It is, of course, easy to understand Sherrington's desire for
contrast with some previous stage of biological knowledge. The
obvious can be interesting in perspective and, if one imagines
oneself faced with the author's task of writing a *Man on his
Nature*, then surely one would also feel the need for a platform
to return to every now and then before making a fresh effort in a
new direction. From the author's point of view moments of rest
would be more precious than the reader's need for contrast.

The panoramic part of the book begins to gather momentum
with the third chapter dealing with a presentation of 'Life in
little', the results of optic magnification. Coming from the pre-
microscopic era, 'Fernel seeing man, his type of inseparable
unity of the "life principle" disrupted into billions of microscopic
lives, may well ask to be shown, not only that these component
unit-lives are demonstrable as "lives", but that this mass-life
of the body and its organs is built up from them. He would learn
that the study of physiology now commonly proceeds on that
assumption and never finds it fail. . . . If a definition has to
exclude as well as to include, it must lean on a logical boundary
of what it defines; the term life has no such boundary from
lifeless.'

This standpoint means giving a leading rôle to 'evolution', a
concept which, after Darwin, Wallace, and Mendel, and up to
the present time, has been of such overwhelming importance in
general biology that no other generalization in this field can
rival its hegemony. In the example quoted above, Sherrington

described ontogenetic evolution in one specific case. He returns to evolutional problems in many contexts and clearly defines his viewpoint: 'the key of the problem is not psychical. Chemistry holds the key.' Today we have seen this attitude justified in the work of Crick, Wilkins, and Watson on the genetic code of information as laid down in the nucleic acids rewarded with the Nobel prize in medicine (1962). Sherrington, being concerned throughout his book just as much with mind as with matter, boldly faces one of his leading questions: is mind a product of evolution? This question is so essential because it stands at the entrance to a group of problems concerning mind and matter all of which engage him to the very core of his being, and much depends upon how the first one of them is answered. He has no hesitation on that point. The story of evolution tells us that living things are busy becoming something other than what they are all the time and mind is no exception. It is part of the tide of change. It seems to have arisen in connection with the motor act, when motor integration progressed and became evolved. It had survival value and the biological advantage it conferred on the concrete individual was improvement of control of the motor act. 'What the mind is concerned with is not the act but the aim.' This is another way of defining 'control'.

Sherrington's attitude is an evolutionary monism or pantheism since no line is drawn between life and lifeless, and in life's history of two thousand million years, mind, soul, psyche— these terms are not separated—are regarded as having emerged in the general development of cell aggregates into bodies with brains. In his own words: 'The appearance of a recognizable mind in the soma would then be not a creation *de novo* but a development of mind from unrecognizable into recognizable. It is at this point therefore that on these admissions we become committed to dualism. But while accepting this duality (of energy and mind) we remember that Nature in instance after instance dealing with this duality treats it as a unity.' Hence Sherrington's dualism is a purely pragmatic acceptance of energy and mind as phenomena of two categories. 'Pragmatic judgement here, as often, ranges itself beside Nature's practice. Pragmatic judgement accepts ourselves as compounds of energy and mind.'

Sherrington is not unaware of the epistemological problems

involved because of mind being our only channel of information, but he does not want to discuss this question which has been amply expounded by the philosophers from Leibnitz, Berkeley, and Hume onwards. It can hardly be out of ignorance that on the whole he ignores philosophers. He wants to be, as he says, 'the man in the street'. He examines the situation and finds that natural science is consistent in its application of the energy concept, including its application to living material. 'The mental is not examinable as a form of energy.' It lies outside natural science, and of the relation between thoughts and the brain we only know of gross correlations in time and space. Countless experiences provide us with a general localization of the mind to the brain, but then mind has no lower limit accessible to definition. It comes from nothing and returns to nothing. To apply common-sense dualism alongside theoretical unity 'may be taken either as sanity or superficiality or perhaps both'. His examination of the scientific as distinct from philosophical evidence has led him to this final standpoint: 'the duality is there; and combination is there, but the footing on which the combination rests . . . is for our enquiry still to seek. . . . Where our knowledge halts our description will resort to metaphor. Long will man's fancy deal with the tie between body and mind by metaphor and often half forget a while that metaphor it is. Regarding this problem will a day come when metaphors can be dispensed with?'

Sherrington's attitude should not be confused with the dualism of theology nor be cited as an example of revealed insight. He emphasizes that 'the mind by its own unaided vision looking at our world does not find that world resolve into First Cause and the things which That has created and maintains. It finds, so far as I can exercise "its" vision, that our world resolves itself into energy and mind.' Sherrington praises Newton's essential modernity in that he accepted what he declared he could not account for.' Our parable,' he says, 'would preach acceptance of energy and mind as a working biological unity although we cannot describe the how of that unity.'

One further consequence of Sherrington's evolutionary attitude to all these problems is the anthropomorphic concept that the human mind is the limit which life has reached in complexity and perfection.

If, as is sometimes said, history is the tracing of past purposes, here is a history which might, while telling of past purpose, whisper to us of future purpose. It would seem so to whisper to us that we have been Earth's purpose. We must not let that flatter us too far. It adds 'not as an end but as a means to a further end'. Moreover our reflexion adds that history read backwards will whisper the same answer to each of its products which shall make that enquiry of it.

The religiosity that pervades *Man on his Nature* has sometimes been held to be a biologist's justification of the truth of Revealed Religion, the reason being Sherrington's defence of dualism. This is sheer wishful thinking, because Sherrington himself has made every possible effort to explain the pragmatical nature of his concepts. His is a Natural Religion and if a name for describing his standpoint be wanted, it is 'Evolutionary Pantheism'. Mind and energy are two concepts, formulated by mind. We arrive at them from a study of evolution in which they go together as a unity and it is impossible for us to know where in the series mind ends or begins. For all we know, mind may be an attribute of matter. What we recognize is merely the final product of evolution.

When on the other hand the mind-concept is so applied as to insert into the human individual an immortal soul, . . . a trespass is committed. . . . As an assertion on the plane of Natural Knowledge it is an irrational blow at the solidarity of the individual; it seems aimed against that very harmony which unites the concepts [energy and mind] as sister-concepts. . . . Together they make up the sum total for us; they are all we have. We called them disparate and incommensurable. Are they then absolutely apart? . . . They have this in common. . . . they are both concepts; they both of them are parts of knowledge of one mind. They are thus therefore distinguished, but are not sundered. Nature in evolving us makes them two parts of the knowledge of one mind and that one mind our own. We are the tie between them. Perhaps we exist for that.

Sherrington's evolutionary pantheism, though leaving God and the Immortal Soul to Revealed Religion (its evidence 'rests on grounds we do not enter upon here', he says), nevertheless encounters all the ethical problems that belong to the sphere of mind, not excluding the rôle of evil. No revealed Lucifer is necessary to expose Nature's malevolence. Cruelty is inherent in

the design, if we look upon it from our own standpoint. Life is
not a sacred thing, nature is non-moral, not immoral. We know
this well. But what has happened when at a certain stage of
development Nature has evolved minds with concepts which by
a common term are known as 'values', such as 'sacred', 'evil',
'immoral'? 'Whence has he [Man] got them? Inventions of his
own? Conventions? How far can he trust them? Can *a priori*
principles suffice to base them?' Sherrington replies: 'They are
under test. They are in the making, even more than is the rest
that he is.' He cannot answer the questions raised but seems to
believe that awareness of the sense of pain is at the root of it.
'Human life has among its privileges that of pre-eminence of
pain.' Thus he makes suffering the evolutionary basis of the
distinction between good and evil. We carry in our inheritance
a social and a predatory streak. Whither does evolution lead us?
Whatever the answer, it is certain that 'the ascendancy of
homo praedatorius would spell ruin to man'.

Sherrington thus thinks of values as products of evolution
that have come to stay. The great revealed religions have
played a leading rôle in developing this aspect of mind. They
have moved and organized communities by their emotional
appeal. What about Natural Religion? Sherrington replies:

[it] has convictions; it must therefore have emotion. Its convictions
entertain 'values' and the 'values' constrain emotion. We saw that
one of its 'values' is Beauty. Also it knows the sentiment of wonder.
. . . And there is Truth. Natural Religion along with the great religions
holds 'truth' a value. . . . Compared with a situation where the human
mind beset with its perplexities had higher mind and higher personality than itself to lean on and to seek counsel from, this other situation
where it has no appeal and no resort for help beyond itself, has, we
may think, an element of enhanced tragedy and pathos. To set against
that, it is a situation which transforms the human spirit's task almost
beyond recognition, to one of loftier responsibility.

Finally, Sherrington discusses the problem of Hume's
Dialogue, whether the pain of the world is offset by its joy.
Nature, he says, has revealed to us values such as Truth,
Charity, and Beauty.

Surely these are compensations to us for much. And will not this
compensation grow? Charity will grow; Truth grows; and even as

Truth so Beauty. Music as her ear grows finer embraces what once were discords. The mind which began by being one thing has truly—as so often in evolution—gone on to being another thing. Even should man in the cataclysm of Nature be doomed to disappear and man's mind with it, man will have had his compensation: to have glimpsed a coherent world and himself as item in it. To have heard for a moment a harmony wherein he is a note. And to listen to a harmony is to commune with its Composer?

This statement ends with a question mark in order to indicate, I assume, where the borderland of belief lies.

Man on his Nature is Sherrington's *credo* and I have chosen to summarize it rather than examine its concepts. It shows from where he drew 'his salve for existence' and how much science meant for him; it displays his learning and breadth of knowledge and overwhelms us with his vitality, insight, and sincerity. Sherrington is entitled to be taken at his word when he refuses to call himself a philosopher and prefers to be 'the man in the street', telling passers-by what he has seen and experienced in a life devoted to experimental biology. It is true that Professor Asher of Berne, at the international meeting of neurologists (1931) mentioned in the previous chapter, harangued him as 'the philosopher of the central nervous system', but I am inclined to disagree. Sherrington's mind was that of an artist, complex, intuitive, rich, visual in the extreme, and what kept all this in balance in his career as a scientist was the empirical attitude of the great experimenter living in his work. In the same sense many famous artists have been great experimenters, highly critical of their own results and methods.

His love of poetry was genuine, a secret chamber to which he sometimes withdrew

> turn the key on the lock's pin
> push back the panel and pass in.

There he would revel in strange sights, seeking expressions for them with the true poet's love of words and images.

> Lodging bewitched! erst there to wake
> was to pawn day for folly's sake!
> There, pulse athrob and sense aswoon,
> light love danced naked at high noon

> above her pictured self, that played
> in the sheened floor and spun and swayed,
> or paused the while pent passion's note
> steadied the curve of her white throat,
> and bliss to bliss was made aware
> beneath the cloud of her loosed hair.

This is from *The Assaying of Brabantius*, his consummate poem, a day of meeting with a world of beauty and desire which, alas, he had to forsake for creation in a different field. Yet he did not feel that he had dwelt in that other world in vain. Returning to his life of experimentation and again

> entering the city gate
> I found the loud street passionate
> with meanings new, and from men's eyes
> read trulier in humbler wise,
> and in fresh ambit understood
> the poignancy of ill and good.

Poetry gave him a wisdom and understanding of men and their ways, respect for values, and when in his old age he wrote *Man on his Nature* it was still with him as a source of inspiration on which he drew for exaltation and passion in his approach to Nature as revealed to the enquiring mind of Man.

Although Sherrington's verse sometimes grew strained with esoteric words piled up in defiance of interpretation to suit rhyme, at other times he found happy expressions for his emotions in lyrics of true beauty. They were often written in a mood of tender sadness during the First World War when his thoughts turned to the young men in the trenches, or when he recalled someone who

> died that other lives might grow
> that other feet than his step free
> in their loved lands, as ours now go,
> where his steps never more shall be

This poem begins

> Now the red thorn's sunrise fire,
> laburnums all sweep golden-hung,

> the thrush as never could he tire
> essays his thrice-anointed tongue;
> above the lasher's pool the sedge
> lifts, breaking the bright waters through;
> green is the wear of every hedge
> and skies as mavis eggs are blue.

Oxford scenery was often recalled against that same background of emptiness and tragedy:

> Ay, oil the hinges of the ancient gate,
> keep burnished bright the goblet's silvern state
> against the hour shall hail the soldiers home.
> Thou, stately tower, from high that sawst them go,
> and hast full many doughty scenes and fair
> watched and swung bells above, shattering the air
> to honour heroes, thou too waitst as though
> thou standst of our poor presence scarcely ware,
> catching afar the filial bugles blow.

The 'stately tower' was that of Magdalen, his own college at Oxford, to which he became attached in 1913 as Waynflete Professor in his subject. The *Assaying of Brabantius* was composed at Liverpool but this city is not reflected in any of his poems. Most of them are undated but it is a fair guess that, when the main theme is love, they belong to an earlier period of his life than the War Years. Oxford spoke to him in a different way,

> . . . with one voice sole, with accents many,
> tongued turret and tongued stream, tracked pasture fenny,
> and cloister spirit trod, and centuried tree,
> and, bondsmen loosed in Time's tranquillity,
> thy bell-discharged hours. If wharfage any
> thine 'tis where Age shall, nursing late his penny,
> smile at long last to hand him Charon's fee.
> And now, by me laden with singing and young laughter,
> and, higher, a wide-flung casement casts afloat
> pulses of waltz the which white robes sway after;
> sworn Priest of Beauty, these thy shrines among,
> that kneelst with old folk and that dancest with young.

This is the old man whom we met in the first chapter of this book, devoted to his memory, and to whom we now bid farewell.

Notes and References

Chapter 1
Some of the major sources of biographical information are listed below, others have been mentioned in the Preface. The *Dictionary of National Biography* and Sharpey-Schafer's *History of the Physiological Society* (Suppl., *J. Physiol.*, 1927) have been regularly consulted for information on Sherrington's contemporaries.

ADRIAN. Sherrington Memorial Lecture. *Proc. Roy. Soc. Med.*, 1957, *50*, 991.

ANDRADE, E. N. Da C. Sherrington as a Master of Words. *The Caian*, 1958, p. 85.

BREMER, F. Charles Scott Sherrington. *Les Prix Nobel de Médecine*, Union Européenne d'Edition, Monaco, 1962.

COHEN OF BIRKENHEAD. *Sherrington, Physiologist, Philosopher and Poet*. Liverpool University Press, 1958.

CREED, R. S. Obituary notice. *Brit. J. Psychol.*, 1953, *44*, 1.

DENNY-BROWN, D. Charles Scott Sherrington. *Amer. J. Psychol.*, 1952, *65*, 474.

DENNY-BROWN, D. The Sherrington School of Physiology. *J. Neurophysiol.*, 1957, *20*, 543.

ECCLES, J. C. Obituary. *Brit. J. Phil. Sci.*, 1952, *3*, 298.

FORBES, A. Memorial Tribute. *J. Clin. Neurophysiol. EEG.*, 1952, *4*, 213.

FULTON, J. F., Obituary. *The Lancet*, 1952, *262*, 569.

LIDDELL, E. G. T. Charles Scott Sherrington. *Obituary Notices of Fellows of the Royal Society*, 1952, *8*, 241.

PENFIELD, W. Sir Charles Sherrington, Poet and Philosopher. *Brain*, 1957, *80/III*, 402.

SHERRINGTON, C. E. R. 'Memories for private circulation', delivered as the Beaumont Lecture (Yale University, November 15, 1957).

SHERRINGTON, C. S. 'Marginalia' in *Essays, etc., written in Honour of Charles Singer*. Vol. II, Oxford University Press, 1953.

WIGGERS, C. J. Some Significant Advances in Cardiac Physiology during the Nineteenth Century. *Hist. Med.*, 1960, *34*, 1. (Contains the reference to Gaskell's work.)

Chapter 2
The classical books and papers on anatomy and physiology, referred to in the text, can easily be traced from the few references given

below. A bibliography of Sherrington has been compiled by the late Professor John F. Fulton and was included in Denny-Brown's *Selected Writings,* referred to below. It was republished and amended by Lord Cohen of Birkenhead in his book referred to above.

CANGUILHEM, G. *La formation du concept de réflexe aux XVIIe et XVIIIe siècles.* Presses Univ. de France, 1955.

FULTON, J. F. *Physiology of the Nervous System.* Oxford University Press, New York, 3rd Ed., 1949.

LIDDELL, E. G. T. *The Discovery of Reflexes.* Clarendon Press, Oxford, 1960.

PUPILLI, G. C., and FADIGA, E. The Origins of Electrophysiology. *J. of World History,* 1963, 7/2, 549.

RAMÓN Y CAJAL, S. *Recollections of my life.* Transl by E. Horne Craigie. Edited in 2 vols. as *Memoirs Amer. Phil. Soc.,* Philadelphia, 1937. This book was reviewed by Sherrington under the title 'Scientific Endeavour and Inferiority Complex' in *Nature,* 1937, *140,* Suppl.

SHERRINGTON, C. S. 'A Memoir of Dr Cajal' was published in *Explorers of the human brain. The life of Santiago Ramón y Cajal,* ed. Dorothy F. Cannon. Henry Schuman, New York, 1949.

Chapter 3

For the early development of Sherrington's concepts one of the best sources is his extensive contribution to Schäfer's *Textbook of Physiology,* vol. 2, Pentland, London and Edinburgh, 1900. It contains in addition everything known in neurophysiology, including the sense organs, at the time of writing, and can justly be called a piece of first-rate scholarship.

CREED, R. S., DENNY-BROWN, D., ECCLES, J. C., LIDDELL, E. G. T., and SHERRINGTON, C. S. *Reflex Activity of the Spinal Cord.* Clarendon Press, Oxford, 1932.

DENNY-BROWN, D. *Selected Writings of Sir Charles Sherrington.* Hamish Hamilton, London, 1939.

ECCLES, J. C. Some Aspects of Sherrington's Contribution to Neurophysiology. *Notes and Records of the Roy. Soc.,* 1957, *12,* 216.

ERLANGER, J., and GASSER, H. S. *Electrical Signs of Nervous Activity.* University of Pennsylvania Press, Philadelphia, 1937.

FULTON, J. F. *Muscle Contraction and the Reflex Control of Movement.* Williams & Wilkins, Baltimore, 1926.

SHERRINGTON, C. S. *The Integrative Action of the Nervous System.* Silliman Lectures (Yale University Press, New Haven); Constable, London, 1906.

SHERRINGTON, C. S. Inhibition as a Co-ordinative Factor. *Les Prix Nobel,* Norstedt & Söner, Stockholm, 1932.

Chapter 4

The references given below are restricted to summaries dealing with the cerebellum, cerebral localization and the work of Magnus and de Kleijn.

Dow, R. S. and Moruzzi, G. *The Physiology and Pathology of the Cerebellum.* University of Minnesota Press, 1958.

Magnus, R. *Die Körperstellung.* Springer, Berlin, 1924.

Penfield, W. and Erickson, T. C. *Epilepsy and Cerebral Localization.* Charles D. Thomas, Springfield, 1941.

Chapter 5

Adrian, E. D. *The Basis of Sensation. The Action of Sense Organs.* Christophers, London, 1928.

Adrian, E. D. *The Mechanism of Nervous Action. Electrical Studies of the Neurone.* Clarendon Press, Oxford, 1932.

Denny-Brown, D. On the Nature of Postural Reflexes. *Proc. Roy. Soc.*, 1929, *B104*, 252.

Eccles, J. C. *The Neurophysiological Basis of Mind.* Clarendon Press, Oxford, 1957.

Granit, R. *Receptors and Sensory Perception.* Silliman Lectures. Yale University Press, 1955.

Hoffmann, P. *Untersuchungen über die Eigenreflexe (Sehnenreflexe) menschlicher Muskeln.* Springer, Berlin, 1922.

Lloyd, D. P. C. On Reflex Actions of Muscular Origin. Patterns of Organization in the Central Nervous System. *Proc. Ass. Res. Nerv. Ment. Disease*, 1950, *30*, 48.

Lorente de Nó, R. Transmission of Impulses through Cranial Motor Nuclei. *J. Neurophysiol.*, 1939, *2*, 402.

Piper, H. *Die Elektrophysiologie menschlicher Muskeln.* Springer, Berlin, 1912.

Chapter 6

The reference to Florey is to a Symposium dealing with inhibition in all its aspects.

Florey, E., Editor. *Nervous Inhibition.* Pergamon Press, London, 1961.

Hodgkin, A. L. The Ionic Basis of Electrical Activity in Nerve and Muscle. *Biol. Rev.*, 1951, *26*, 339.

Eccles, J. C. *The Physiology of Nerve Cells.* Johns Hopkins Press, Baltimore, 1957.

Kuffler, S. W. Excitation and Inhibition in Single Nerve Cells. *Harvey Lectures*, 1960, *54*, 176.

Chapter 7

The reader interested in Sherrington's work on tone and plasticity will find it described in the papers published in the *Quart. J. Exp. Physiol.* between 1909 and 1913 (see Bibliography, quoted above). Ideas on muscle tone up to 1930 have been reviewed by Bremer (below). The gamma-spindle work is of a later date and was first extensively summarized by the author in his Silliman Lectures, quoted above. The two Symposia quoted below present latest developments in both anatomy and physiology.

BARKER, D., Editor. *Symposium on Muscle Receptors.* Hong Kong University Press, Hong Kong, 1962.

BREMER, F. Le Tonus Musculaire. *Annal. Physiol. et Physico-Chem. Biol.*, 1932, 8, 199.

GRANIT, R., Editor. *Muscular Afferents and Motor Control. Nobel Symposium* I. Almqvist & Wiksell, Stockholm, 1966.

Chapter 8

SHERRINGTON, C. S. *The Assaying of Brabantius and Other Verse.* Oxford University Press, 1925.

SHERRINGTON, C. S. *Goethe on Nature and Science.* Cambridge University Press, 1942.

ERRINGTON, C. S. *The Endeavour of Jean Fernel.* Cambridge University Press, 1946.

SHERRINGTON, C. S. *Man on his Nature.* Cambridge University Press, 1941.

SHERRINGTON, C. S. Poems printed in the *Cornhill Magazine*, vols. 154 (1936), p. 140, and 155 (1937), pp. 38 and 701.

Index